IMAGES of
BART'S

IMAGES of BART'S

An Illustrated History of
St Bartholomew's Hospital
in the City of London

Geoffrey Yeo

Historical Publications Ltd
In association with
the Archives Department
St Bartholomew's Hospital

First published 1992
by Historical Publications Ltd
32 Ellington Street, London N7 8PL
(Telephone 071–607 1628)

in association with
the Archives Department
St Bartholomew's Hospital, London.

ISBN 0 948667 17 6

Designed and typeset by
Historical Publications Ltd
and Fakenham Photosetting

Printed in Hong Kong
by the South China Printing Company

*The drawing on the title page
depicts the tomb of Rahere, the founder
of the Hospital, in the church of
St Bartholomew the Great.*

CONTENTS

ACKNOWLEDGEMENTS

Many people have offered assistance in the preparation of this book. I am especially grateful to my colleague Mrs Judith Etherton, Assistant District Archivist; to Mr Antony Wallace, Miss Mary Walker and Miss Sybil Allen, retired members of the Hospital staff who have worked for several years as voluntary helpers in the Archives; and to Dr Julian Axe, Secretary and Registrar of the Medical College; Dr John Farwell, District Pharmaceutical Officer; Miss Theodora Hampton, Managing Editor, *Barts Journal*; Dr David Lowe, Senior Lecturer in Histopathology; Miss Janina Morris, Medical College Librarian; the Revd Michael Whawell, Vicar of St Bartholomew the Less; and Dr David Wilkinson, Consultant Anaesthetist and Chairman of the Archives Committee. Without their help and support the book could not have been written. I am also grateful to Mrs Patricia Falcini and Miss Barbara Gower, who kindly gave up their leisure time to provide clerical assistance; to the League of St Bartholomew's Nurses, for valuable help with publicity; and to the Governors of the House of the Poor in West Smithfield (the Voluntary Hospital of St Bartholomew), for offering to underwrite the publication.

Geoffrey Yeo
May 1992

Introduction

St Bartholomew's is one of the oldest and most distinguished hospitals in the world. It is unique among London hospitals in having a continuous history of patient care over more than eight and a half centuries, and it is still located on the very same site where it was founded by Rahere in the year 1123. After 400 years as a monastic hospital it was re-established on a secular basis and was granted a new charter by King Henry VIII in the winter of 1546–7. These changes gave the Hospital a President, a Treasurer and a Board of Governors. As time passed the President became more of a figurehead, and the Treasurer became in effect the chairman of the Governors, with the Clerk as his chief executive officer; but the constitution established by King Henry's charter survived with only minor changes until the Hospital became part of the National Health Service in 1948.

Over the years St Bartholomew's has grown. The buildings of Rahere's time cannot have been large; they probably stood somewhere near the site now occupied by the North Wing of the Hospital. In the early 1540s there were just 45 beds in total; 450 years later St Bartholomew's admitted over 20,000 in-patients annually, besides treating about 175,000 out-patients and more than 50,000 accident and emergency patients every year. Continuing advances in medical and nursing care, and in education and research, have ensured that the Hospital maintains its international reputation.

In recent years the pace of change has accelerated. St Bartholomew's became associated with St Mark's Hospital in 1973, and with the former Hackney Group hospitals in April 1974. Management of the Hospital ceased to be the responsibility of the Board of Governors in 1974. Since then the services offered by St Bartholomew's on its historic site in the City of London have been integrated with those of its associated hospitals. In 1991 Government approval was received for the establishment of a self-governing trust with the title 'The Barts NHS Trust'. It was decided in 1992 that the Homerton Hospital, opened in Hackney in 1986, should become known as 'St Bartholomew's Hospital at Homerton', and that the original site in the City should become 'St Bartholomew's Hospital at Smithfield'.

This book is intended to give an impression, in words and pictures, of the life and work of St Bartholomew's on its ancient site over many years. The text provides an outline of its architectural history and of the development of many different aspects of its work. The illustrations are mainly from the nineteenth and twentieth centuries; they have been selected from the varied holdings in the Hospital Archives, and many have not been published before. The selection of topics has not been easy, and much that might have been included has had to be omitted for reasons of space. The book does not endeavour to offer the same wealth of detail as V.C. Medvei and J.L. Thornton's *The Royal Hospital of St Bartholomew 1123–1973*, published in 1974; still less does it attempt to provide the full scholarly history which is still much needed; but I hope that it will bring pleasure, and enlightenment, to all who have an interest in London's greatest hospital.

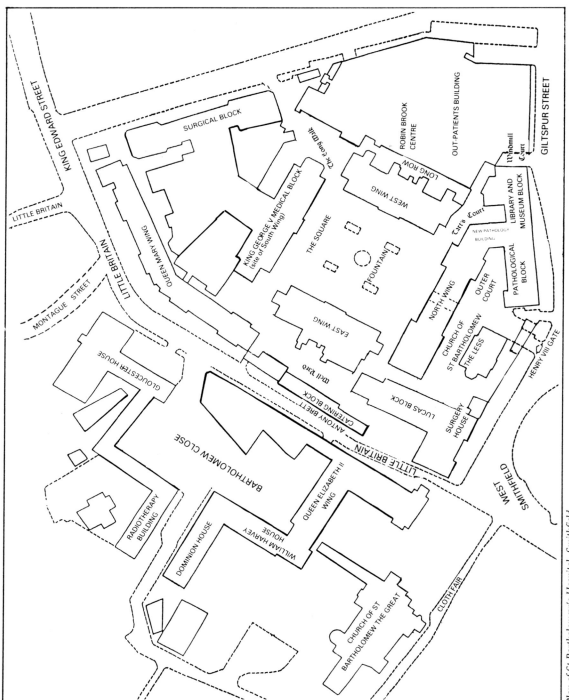

Plan of St Bartholomew's Hospital, Smithfield

SMITHFIELD

The site chosen for the foundation of St Bartholomew's Hospital was in Smithfield, which in 1123 was a piece of marshy ground outside the walls of the City. It is often called 'West Smithfield', to distinguish it from East Smithfield near the Tower of London. According to legend the site was selected, not by Rahere, but by Saint Bartholomew himself. The traditional account of the foundation is recorded in a manuscript in the British Library. Rahere, a man 'born of low lineage' who had become an attendant of King Henry I, had fallen ill while in Rome on a pilgrimage. He vowed that if his health were restored, he would found a hospital for the poor. After his recovery he had a vision of a majestic figure, who announced that he was Bartholomew, one of the twelve apostles of Jesus Christ, and had come to assist Rahere and to open to him "the secret mysteries of heaven"."Know me truly", the Saint continued, "to have chosen a place in the suburbs of London, at Smithfield, where in my name you shall found a church, and it shall be the house of God".

Later writers added to this legend, suggesting that Rahere was the king's jester, and that the scene of his vision was on the Isola Tiberina in Rome, a traditional place of healing where there is an ancient church dedicated to St Bartholomew. None of this appears in the original account. However the original manuscript does record that Rahere returned to

St Bartholomew's Hospital viewed from West Smithfield, 1720.

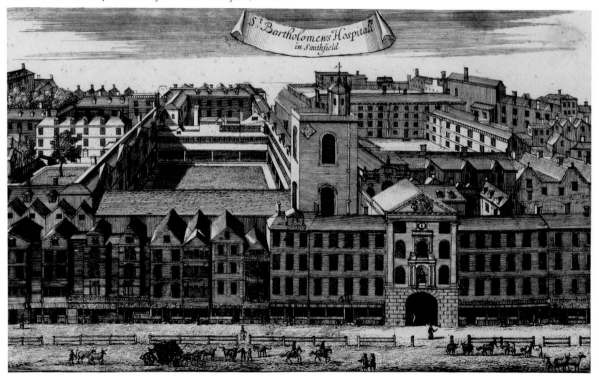

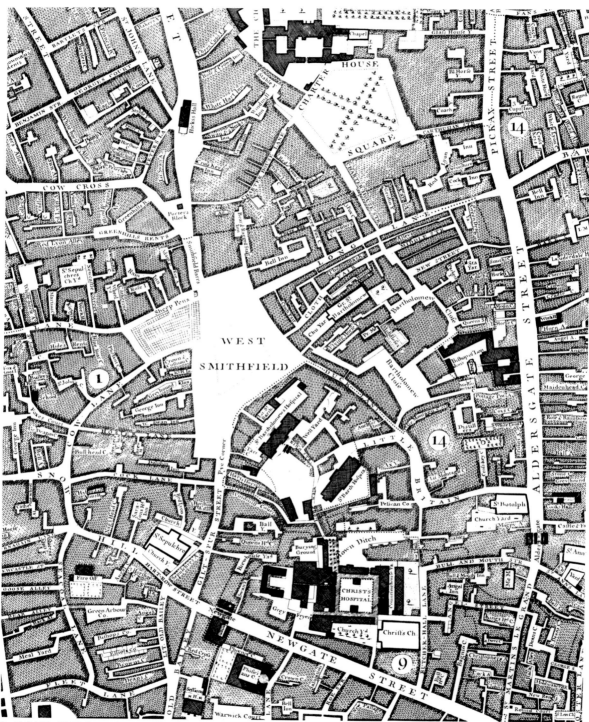

Smithfield in 1745. Rocque's map of London.

Smithfield Market, c.1830; engraved by T. Barber from a drawing by Thomas H. Shepherd.

London, and in March 1123 established both a church (now the parish church of St Bartholomew the Great) and a hospital on the site which had been indicated to him.

According to William Fitzstephen, a twelfth-century writer, Smithfield was indeed a 'smooth field'; it is evident that in Rahere's time it was flat ground, on the very edge of the built-up area of London, with countryside to the north and west. On the far side, where the meat market was built many years later, was a pond known as the Horse Pool. At the beginning of the fifteenth century there was still a coppice of trees on the west side of Smithfield. Known as 'The Elms', it was the site of gallows where criminals were executed. The surroundings of Smithfield were built over between c.1400 and c.1600, and the open space in the centre was first paved in 1615.

In the fourteenth and fifteenth centuries Smithfield was used for tournaments, where knights came to joust in the presence of the king. More infamously, it was also the place where heretics were burnt at the stake. The first burnings took place about 1400, but Smithfield became most notorious in the reign of Queen Mary (1553–8), when John Rogers, John Bradford, John Philpot and many

other protestants were put to death there. A plaque in Smithfield, on the wall of the Hospital near the corner of Little Britain, commemorates their martyrdom; another plaque nearby commemorates the execution in 1305 of the Scottish patriot William Wallace, who had fought against the English King Edward I.

Every summer from the twelfth century until 1854 Smithfield was the scene of the famous Bartholomew Fair, which in the late middle ages was one of the largest cloth trading fairs in England. The Fair is often said to have begun in the reign of King Henry II (1154–89), but a charter granted to St Bartholomew's in 1133 mentions Bartholomew Fair as being already in existence. Originally a three-day event held on the feast of St Bartholomew (24 August) and the days immediately before and after, the Fair was later extended into September. By the early seventeenth century, when Ben Jonson wrote his play *Bartholomew Fair*, the cloth merchants had taken their business elsewhere, and the Fair was noted for puppet shows, pedlars and pickpockets rather than for serious trading. The street name

(Overleaf): *Bartholomew Fair, 1807; engraved by Rowlandson from a drawing by John Nixon.*

The east side of Smithfield, c.1880, with the entrance gateway to the church of St Bartholomew the Great.

Cloth Fair survives as a reminder of its original purpose. St Bartholomew's Hospital played no part in the running of the Fair, but in Ben Jonson's time it was able to collect rent for standings because the Fair had expanded beyond Smithfield into the Hospital precincts. In the nineteenth century the Fair declined and eventually ceased altogether, though the name has occasionally been revived for other festivities in Smithfield, such as the celebrations held in 1923 to mark the Hospital's 800th anniversary.

Besides the annual Fair, regular livestock markets took place in Smithfield throughout the year. A horse and cattle market was already established there by 1123. Until the eighteenth century it was confined to the summer months because there was no winter feeding for the animals which were herded from all parts of the country. On arrival the cattle, sheep and pigs were tethered and penned in the open space in front of the Hospital to be auctioned, when they would be driven through the surrounding roads to the slaughter-houses in Newgate Street. By the mid nineteenth century the market was becoming too large for the area. Complaints about the noise and smells, combined with inflammatory newspaper reports of accidents involving runaway bulls, led to increasing public demands for its closure.

In the 1830s Charles Dickens described the market in *Oliver Twist*:

'The ground was covered nearly ankle-deep with filth and mire; a thick steam, perpetually rising from the reeking bodies of the cattle, and mingling with the fog, which seemed to rest upon the chimney-tops, hung heavily above. All the pens in the centre of the large area, and as many temporary pens as could be crowded into the vacant space, were filled with sheep; tied up to posts by the gutter side were long lines of beasts and oxen, three or four deep. Countrymen, butchers, drovers, hawkers, boys, thieves, idlers and vagabonds of every low grade, were mingled together in a mass; ...the hideous and discordant din that resounded from every corner of the market, and the unwashed, unshaven, squalid and dirty figures constantly running to and fro and bursting in and out of the throng, rendered it a stunning and bewildering scene.'

For many centuries the chaos of the market was familiar to every visitor to St Bartholomew's Hospital, and the noise of the animals formed the regular accompaniment to the Hospital's work. The livestock market was held in Smithfield for the last time

'Bartholomew Fair' revived in Smithfield to mark the 800th anniversary of the foundation of the Hospital, 1923.

Smithfield, c.1926–7, with the entrance to the goods station in the foreground.

Aerial view of Smithfield, c.1930–5. The Hospital buildings are in the centre of the photograph.

in 1855; thereafter it was relocated in Copenhagen Fields, near Islington. Ten years later work began on the construction of the Central Meat Market in Smithfield which was completed in 1868. At the same time as the market was built, a subterranean railway was constructed to bring meat to Smithfield and a goods station opened with a spiral access ramp for horse-drawn vehicles. The station continued to function until 1962, but was subsequently converted into an underground car park. The garden in the centre of Smithfield was opened in 1872–3.

The buildings of St Bartholomew's Hospital have occupied the south side of Smithfield since the middle ages. Old prints of Smithfield Market show terraces of houses along the Hospital's frontage on either side of the Henry VIII Gate. These houses were the property of the Hospital and were let to tenants. Many of them were demolished in 1842 when the existing screen wall was built. Others were pulled down later in the nineteenth century and the last of the old houses were removed in 1907.

THE HENRY VIII GATE

The magnificent Henry VIII Gate, facing north onto the open space of Smithfield, was built in 1702. Long before this date the main entrance to the Hospital precinct was on this site; and it is possible that it was located there as early as the twelfth century.

In August 1701 the Board of Governors gave instructions for the north gate to be rebuilt and flanked with new tenements at higher rents to replace those already on the site. In March 1702 the Governors' minute book recorded an agreement 'with Edward Strong junior, mason, to erect and build the front of this Hospital's north gate in Smithfield with Purbeck stone, according to the model drawn by the said Edward Strong...for the sum of £550'. Edward Strong came from a notable family of stonemasons; his uncle had been chief mason to Sir Christopher Wren, and he himself had worked under Wren at St Paul's Cathedral. The building work was completed in the late spring of 1703, but the cost proved to be considerably higher than the original estimate: £1493 had already been spent by Michaelmas 1702, and a further £1320 was spent before the Gate and the adjoining houses were finished. A clock to adorn the facade of the Gate was made by Richard Horton in 1702.

Above the archway stands a statue of King Henry VIII: the only such statue in a public place in London. The statue is the work of the sculptor Francis Bird and is contemporary with the Gate; the King's crown and sceptre were made in 1987 by John Sambrook, the crown replacing a decayed Victorian one. Above the King are two further sculptures, one holding a crutch, the other with its right arm in a sling. These are thought to be allegorical figures of Lameness and Disease.

The inscription on the Gate reads 'St Bartholomew's Hospitall, founded by Rahere anno 1102, refounded by K. Henry VIII 1546. This front was rebuilt anno 1702 in the first year of Queen Anne; Sir Wm. Prichard K[nigh]t and Alder[man], President; John Nicoll Esq., Treasurer'. The date '1102' is an error, for the Hospital was actually founded in 1123. John Stow's *Survey of London*, first published in 1598, wrongly stated that St Bartholomew's Hospital was established in 1102, and the mistake

The Henry VIII Gate, with houses on both sides, 1816; drawn and engraved by T. Higham.

gained wide circulation; as late as the 1840s an inscription was placed on what is now Lucas Block, giving Stow's date for the founding of the Hospital instead of the correct one.

In 1833–4 the Gate was substantially reconstructed. The eighteenth century facade overlooking West Smithfield remained unaltered, but the houses immediately adjoining the Gate were demolished, and ground and first floor rooms were

The Henry VIII Gate seen from Smithfield, 1899.

The inner archway of the Gate at night, c.1939–40.

added on either side of the central arch. The rear of the Gate was remodelled and faced with stone at the same time.

The Gate has had many uses. In 1834 it was employed as a residence for the house surgeons, and in the early twentieth century the rooms were lived in by the Hospital beadles and their families. More recently it has been used as office accommodation.

The Gate was restored in 1969 and again in 1985–7 when a Civic Trust commendation was made for the restoration work.

THE CHURCH OF
ST BARTHOLOMEW THE LESS

Just inside the Henry VIII Gate lies the Hospital's parish church of St Bartholomew the Less. The tower and part of the west wall of the church date from the fifteenth century and are the oldest structures which now survive within the Hospital precinct.

Before the Reformation there would appear to have been five chapels within the Hospital, but only one survived the dissolution of the monasteries by Henry VIII. In the winter of 1546–7, when the Hospital was re-founded by royal charter, its precinct was established as the Anglican parish of St Bartholomew the Less, and one of the medieval chapels

Exterior of the church in 1737, before eighteenth century reconstruction.

became the parish church. The original parish boundary followed the line of the boundary of the Hospital in Henry VIII's day, but since 1954 the parish boundary has been extended to include the land on which the Hospital has expanded to the south and east. Bart's is now unique among English hospitals in being a parish in its own right. The parish has its own churchwardens and, since 1958, its parochial church council, which functions independently of the Hospital authorities.

The title of 'Anglican chaplain', found in practically every other hospital in England, does not exist at Bart's. The role is filled by the Vicar of St Bartholomew the Less, who is correctly known as the 'Vicar and Hospitaller'. In the sixteenth century these were originally two separate offices: the Vicar of St Bartholomew the Less, who undertook pastoral care of the parishioners, and the Hospitaller to St Bartholomew's Hospital, who looked after the needs of the patients. However in the time of William Orme, Vicar from 1670 to 1697, the two positions were combined, and they have been held jointly by successive clergy down to the present day. In former times there were a number of tenanted houses in the Hospital precinct, but there are now no parishioners except resident Hospital staff, and the incumbent's main responsibility is for the spiritual welfare of patients within the Hospital.

The church building no longer retains its medieval appearance. The medieval church remained largely intact until 1789–91, when the roof and practically the whole of the interior were demolished and rebuilt to the design of George Dance junior, the Hospital Surveyor. Dance's structure, however,

Interior of the church as designed by George Dance; this engraving was published in 1834 but shows the church as it appeared before Hardwick's alterations in 1823–5.

A Sister playing the church organ, c.1905.

St Bartholomew the Less, c.1929. The field gun in the foreground was brought to Bart's by medical students shortly after the armistice in 1918 and remained in the grounds of the Hospital for many years.

was rapidly attacked by dry rot, and the church was again rebuilt in 1823–5. The architect of the second rebuilding was Thomas Hardwick, and it is chiefly his work that is visible in the church today. Hardwick retained much of Dance's octagonal design for the interior of the church, but reconstructed it using more durable materials, and pulled down all that remained of the medieval building apart from the tower and west end. Some of the monuments from the old building were preserved and reinstated: these included memorials to Robert Balthrope, Queen Elizabeth I's serjeant surgeon (died 1591), and to Anne, wife of Thomas Bodley, the founder of the Bodleian Library at Oxford, whose London house stood within the Hospital precinct in the early seventeenth century.

A curious feature of the church is the height of the floor, most of which is some 75cm above ground level; the reason for this appears to be unknown. Below the west window is a canopied tomb of fifteenth or sixteenth century workmanship, which is now disfigured by an inscription in black marble that once marked the grave of Elizabeth, wife of John Freke, Surgeon to the Hospital from 1729 to 1755. In the floor nearby is a monumental brass commemorating William Markeby and his wife; William Markeby lived in the Hospital precinct and died in July 1439. The sculptured heraldic carvings on the walls above were formerly affixed to the exterior of the south wall of the church, and were probably removed from there during Hardwick's demolition work in the 1820s.

In the tower are three bells: the treble was cast in 1869, but the other two are medieval, and are very probably as old as the tower itself. There is also a sanctus bell dating from 1825. The pulpit, with its carved panels of biblical scenes, dates from 1864. The organ, by Hill, Norman and Beard, was installed in 1930–1 and rebuilt by Noel Mander in 1978 when a new detached console was provided. The stained glass windows depicting the Virgin and Child with St Luke, St Bartholomew and Rahere, and also the war memorial windows, were designed by Hugh Easton and dedicated in 1951; they replaced Victorian glass destroyed in the Second World War. A new doorway for wheelchair patients was opened at the south end of the east wall in 1969.

In earlier centuries attendance at church was compulsory for the nursing staff of the Hospital; patients too were expected to attend every Sunday, unless they were too weak to do so. Now that attendance is no longer obligatory, congregations are smaller, but regular Sunday and weekday services are still held throughout the year, and the church is frequently chosen by members of staff for weddings, for the baptisms of their children, and for memorial services. The Vicar and Hospitaller works in close co-operation with chaplains of other denominations and is available to advise or counsel staff and patients, their relatives and other visitors.

The Outer Court

The Outer Court, which lies between the church of St Bartholomew the Less and the North Wing, occupies the site formerly known as the Cloisters. This name almost certainly dates from the era of the monastic hospital, before its dissolution in the 1540s by King Henry VIII. In 1720 the historian John Strype described 'a passage into Smithfield through a fair Cloister well paved with free stone, on both sides of which are rows of shops mostly taken up by seamstresses and milliners, and over the shops on the walls are the names of benefactors to this Hospital fairly painted; and this Cloister gives entrance into the several wards belonging to this Hospital.'

On 25 September 1729 an order was made for the Cloisters to be demolished, to prepare the ground for the building of the North Wing. The name, however, survived some years; and it is evident that not all the old buildings were pulled down immediately, for in 1897 the *St Bartholomew's Hospital Journal* reported that 'some of the cloisters were still standing within the memory of living persons'.

The Outer Court did not reach its present shape until the early years of the twentieth century. In Victorian times a large square building, connected by a corridor to the North Wing, stood directly opposite the church. In the 1880s and 1890s this building housed the Electrical Department. Its presence gave the appearance of a narrow passageway immediately behind the Henry VIII Gate, in contrast to the open aspect created when it was pulled down and the Pathological Block erected in 1907–9.

Further to the east, the vicarage house of St Bartholomew the Less once stood in the Outer Court beyond the church. When the building now known as Lucas Block was erected in 1842 it lay behind the vicarage house, and the present vista towards Lucas Block along the length of the Outer Court was not opened up until the latter part of the century. When the vicarage was demolished, a garden was created around the church, but this was gradually reduced in size until only a small strip on the south side remained. Plans were made in the early 1990s for a new garden to be laid out on the north side of the church.

The Outer Court, c.1929.

Charles B. Lockwood, Surgeon, in his motor-car in the Outer Court, c.1905. Lockwood was the first member of staff to use a car at Bart's.

The Outer Court in the early nineteenth century: a view looking towards the rear of the Henry VIII Gate.

THE SQUARE

The Square of St Bartholomew's Hospital is one of the finest groups of buildings in London. Its origins can be traced back to the summer of 1723, when the Board of Governors decided that most of the surviving medieval structures on the site should be demolished. The Hospital had remained untouched by the Great Fire of London, but by the early eighteenth century its old buildings were inadequate and dilapidated. A committee was appointed to draw up plans for rebuilding, and among its members was the distinguished architect James Gibbs, who had been elected a Governor a few months earlier.

The committee was slow to act, but in September 1728 it produced a scheme for the first of the new buildings, which would contain a large hall for full meetings of the Board of Governors, a 'counting house' for the despatch of other business, a room for admitting and discharging patients, and a house for the Clerk.

In July 1729 the Governors issued a statement that 'by reason of the great increase of this populous City the Hospital is not large enough to receive the whole number of those poor infirm people who daily apply there for relief...some of the old wards are so decayed that it is necessary to rebuild them...for which reasons the Governors have resolved that all buildings which shall be erected for the future shall be agreeable to one uniform plan'. This plan had been drawn up by Gibbs and approved by the Governors at their meeting on 1 May 1729; it showed four detached wings around a central Square. The South, West and East Wings were to contain the new wards. There were to be twelve wards in each wing, with fourteen beds in each ward. The North

The Square, c.1830; engraved by A. Cruse from a drawing by Thomas H. Shepherd.

Plan of the Square, 1756, with elevations of the North and West Wings.

The Square in winter, 1889. The Fountain and the South Wing are visible behind the trees and flower beds. The shelters had not yet been constructed.

Wing would contain the Great Hall, the Clerk's House, and the other offices mentioned in the scheme produced in 1728. A 'passage for coaches' would run through the centre of the North Wing, with the Great Hall on the first floor above it.

It was to be forty years before the Square was complete. The foundation stone of the North Wing was laid on 9 July 1730, and the building work was probably concluded in 1732, although the interior decoration was not finished until 1738. The South Wing was started in 1736, completed in 1739, and opened for patients in 1740. The construction of the West Wing was authorised by the Governors at their meeting in March 1742, but for some years it proved impossible to obtain all the stone that was needed, and work did not begin in earnest until 1748. The West Wing was finished in 1752, when the Governors ordered 'that the new wards of the third pile of building be used for the reception of women patients only'. On 11 May 1753 the Governors were informed that the wards in this wing had been filled with patients, and that all the expenses of the building work had been met. The East Wing was the last to be erected, and its construction was the slowest. Work on the foundations began in 1757, and the first stone was laid in April 1758, but the building was not ready for internal fitting and

Three doctors in the Square, c.1905. From left to right, W. Bruce Clarke, W. Harrison Cripps and Holburt Waring.

(Above): *Bed patients and visitors in the Square: a summertime view, c.1905.*

(Right): *Patients being wheeled across the Square, c.1929. This scene was probably posed as a publicity photograph.*

furnishing until 1768. The Governors' order for the transfer of patients into the wards in the East Wing is dated March 1769.

The Square as we see it today is still recognisably the work of James Gibbs, despite numerous later alterations. Old prints show stone urns on the balustrades of the four wings, and arches in the four corners of the Square, connecting each pair of buildings. The urns were removed in 1810, and the arches also had to be taken down to allow improved access to the Square. By the 1840s the original Bath stone used for the external masonry of the four wings had decayed, and between 1850 and 1852 it was replaced by Portland stone which the Hospital Surveyor described as 'best adapted for the atmosphere of London'. In 1935 Gibbs's South Wing was demolished and in its place was built the King George V Medical Block, opened in 1937. The main facade of the block was designed to complement the remaining Gibbs buildings, and some of the stone from the old South Wing was re-used, but the Medical Block is taller and less well-proportioned than its predecessor.

Although only three of the four original buildings now survive, the Square is still a magnificent ensemble, and remains the showpiece of the Hospital. The main approach is still, as Gibbs intended, through the archway under the North Wing. As visitors approach the arch, they can look up to the first storey where a stone inscription commemorates the foundation by Rahere (wrongly dated, as on the Henry VIII Gate, to 1102 instead of 1123), the second foundation by King Henry VIII, and the rebuilding to the design of James Gibbs. The stone is a nineteenth century copy of the original inscription placed on the North Wing by order of the Governors in 1752, with additional text giving details of restorations undertaken in 1814–20 and 1851–2. Below, on either side of the arch, two further inscribed stones contain quotations from the Book of Psalms.

Within the archway some of the original Bath stone can still be seen. Most of the interior of the arch, however, takes its present form from a restoration in 1926, when the old vaulted plaster roof was reconstructed in stone, and new stone panels were placed on either side of the doorways, inscribed with the names of Hospital staff who died in the First World War. Names of those who fell in the Second World War were added at a later date. In front of each of the two doors stands an ornamental pillar with a collecting box inscribed 'Remember the Poor's Box'. These have stood in their present position for many years. In the nineteenth century there were 'poor's boxes' affixed to each of the wings of the Hospital, to encourage donations from visitors.

The central area of the Square was left empty in Gibbs's original design but now contains a number of features of a later date. The Fountain was erected in 1859, at which time shrubs and flower beds were planted in the Square. These were removed in 1895 when the shelters were built. The two ornamental lamps in the Square are the survivors of a set of four

The South Wing in 1935, immediately before its demolition.

Bed patients in the Square in springtime, 1939.

The Square in summer, 1939.

Junior doctors and medical students assembled by the Fountain to await the start of the ward rounds, 1906.

matching lamps dating from about 1890. In front of the North Wing are two lead cisterns dated 1782; these were placed in the former Cohen Garden (now the site of the main entrance to the King George V Block) in 1932, and were later moved to the Square.

The exterior stonework of the North Wing was cleaned in 1973, and the East Wing in the 1980s. The magnificent nineteenth century plane trees which formerly adorned the Square had to be removed following storm damage in October 1987. They have been replaced with six maples.

The Square has been a centre of Hospital life ever since it was built. In the summer months beds are brought out into the Square so that patients can enjoy the sunshine – a custom of many years' standing which still continues. Since the 1960s, however, an increasing demand for car parking space has led to the Square being full of parked vehicles for much of the time. Once a year, on the annual View Day on the second Wednesday in May, the cars are removed, and patients, staff and visitors have the opportunity to enjoy the Square at its best. It still offers visual delights which no other London hospital can match.

THE FOUNTAIN

Since 1859 the Fountain has been the focal point of the Square. On hot summer days people congregate around it, to rest, talk, or simply enjoy the pleasant coolness of the water.

Before its construction the site was occupied by a well, which had been built in 1809 with pumping apparatus to supply additional water to the wards. In 1851 Charles Dickens's journal *Household Words* described it as 'an ugly circular pump, which looks like a slice of a worn-out steam boiler with a lamp on the top'. By 1857, however, the Hospital was receiving a fully adequate water supply from the New River Company's works, and the well had fallen out of use. In January 1858 the Governors agreed that the old pump should be sold, and twelve months later their minutes recorded that 'in consequence of the removal of the pump...the Treasurer was asked to take necessary steps to planting the vacant spot'. A proposal to erect a fountain was put before the Governors in September 1859, 'several of the Governors and Medical Staff having expressed a desire to see one placed there'. The decision to construct the Fountain followed a report on the subject by Philip C. Hardwick, the Hospital Surveyor. Hardwick estimated the cost of construction at about £220, with a further £40 for the basin and pipes, and £95 for the carving of the figures. He pointed out that the jet of water would have to be high enough to be seen above the shrubs, which had recently been planted in the Square, and that the cost of a figure group would not be very much greater than 'any merely architectural form of the same height'. The Fountain is Italianate in style but the exact source of Hardwick's inspiration remains unknown. On 11 October 1859 the Governors accepted his design and resolved that the Fountain be erected. The date of its completion is not recorded.

The Fountain quickly became the appointed meeting place for medical staff and students at the start of a ward round. In the *St Bartholomew's Hospital Journal*, July 1930, Archibald Garrod described a typical scene as it occurred daily throughout the late nineteenth and early twentieth centuries. At half past one the housemen, clinical clerks and dressers would be assembled around the Fountain, awaiting

Around the Fountain, 1890.

the arrival of the 'chief'. 'Presently a brougham drawn by a pair of grey horses would drive into the Square...and from it would alight Dr [Samuel] Gee, small and alert, wearing the orthodox frock-coat and tall hat of the Victorian consultant. Then perhaps his private hansom would bring Mr Thomas Smith [Surgeon to the Hospital], and others would arrive in turn. Then students and residents would sort themselves out into groups, following their respective chief, ...and go with him to his ward'. In 1880, when Garrod was a student, they would have been formally dressed, but by 1930 the white coat had become the normal apparel.

In 1988–90 the Fountain underwent substantial repair for the first time since its construction; a new pumping system was installed and damaged stonework was restored.

A boy at the Fountain, 1914.

The Great Hall and the Hogarth Paintings

The splendid Great Hall, on the first floor of the North Wing, was for many years the meeting place of the Board of Governors. Constructed to the design of James Gibbs between 1730 and 1732, it was decorated between 1733 and 1738, and the original colour scheme has been retained. The gilded ceiling is the only known example in England of the work of the French craftsman Jean Baptiste St Michele.

Around the walls are recorded the names of benefactors to the Hospital. The practice of commemorating their generosity in this way was first ordered by the Governors in 1737, and was maintained until 1905. The earliest names to be seen are dated from 1547; these were painted retrospectively in the eighteenth century.

In the south wall is a stained glass window of the seventeenth century depicting King Henry VIII handing to the Lord Mayor of London the charter which re-established the Hospital. On the far wall is another portrait of Henry VIII, copied from a Holbein group of the king with his third wife Jane Seymour and his parents. This picture was given to the Hospital at the time when the Hall was built, and the frame was especially designed for it by James Gibbs and William Hogarth.

The painting of St Bartholomew above the central fireplace is a work of the seventeenth century Flemish school. It shows him holding a flaying knife, the symbol of his martyrdom. Of roughly the same date are the painted statues of a wounded soldier and sailor. Their origin is uncertain, although it is known that they stood in the Hospital Cloisters in the 1650s. By the nineteenth century they had been removed to the North Wing, where they still remain.

The approach to the Great Hall is by the Grand Staircase, adorned with canvases painted by William Hogarth between 1735 and 1737. Hogarth, who had been born near the Hospital, gave the paintings completely free of charge. The scenes depicted are the biblical stories of the Good Samaritan and the Healing of the Sick at the Pool of Bethesda, which

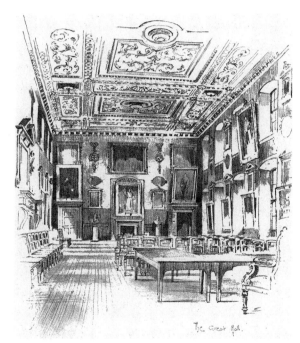

The Great Hall, 1904.

Hogarth chose to fulfil his commission to illustrate the spirit of the Hospital's work. The group of sick people gathered on the left of the Pool gives a good indication of patients in Bart's at the time, whom Hogarth is thought to have used as models.

The three sepia scenes below the main canvases illustrate the story of the founding of the Hospital by Rahere. The first shows Rahere's dream, in which St Bartholomew gave him instructions for the founding of the Hospital; the second, the laying of the first stone; and the third, a patient being brought into the Hospital. These, and the painted

The Grand Staircase and Hogarth paintings; this photograph is undated but was probably taken at about the time of the First World War.

THE GREAT HALL
AS
BART'S SPECIALS SLEEPING QUARTERS.
GENERAL STRIKE _ 1926.

Mattresses and blankets in the Great Hall during the general strike, 1926.

plaster at the top of the staircase with the medallions of Hippocrates and Galen above the doorways, were probably the work of one of Hogarth's students.

The staircase is lit by a contemporary chandelier of carved wood, which was donated by the surgeon John Freke in 1735.

The Great Hall and Hogarth paintings are not generally open to the public, but the Hall can be hired for dinners or receptions.

LUCAS BLOCK AND SURGERY HOUSE

The building now known as Lucas Block was built in 1842 to the design of Philip Hardwick, the Hospital Surveyor, and the northern part was enlarged in 1861 by his son Philip Charles Hardwick. At that time the northern part was used for the reception of out-patients and casualties. The building has had a variety of names over the years, but in the nineteenth and early twentieth centuries it was generally known as the Casualty Block. Other names have included the 'North-East Wing', the 'Abernethy Block' (from Abernethy Ward which occupied the ground floor of the building between 1854 and 1930), and the 'Children's Block' (from the children's wards installed there in the 1950s).

However the name in general use in the last decades of the twentieth century is 'Lucas Block', commemorating Matthias Prime Lucas, President of the Hospital from 1831 to 1848, whose name appears on the stone inscription on the Smithfield facade. A Lucas Ward existed in this block from 1842 to 1930, and when the children's wards were opened in 1954 one of them was also given the same name.

The inscription on the facade also commemorates the founding of the Hospital by Rahere (wrongly dated, as on the Henry VIII Gate and North Wing, to 1102 instead of 1123); the re-foundation by King Henry VIII; the construction of the block in 1842 and its later enlargement. The extension in 1861 was

Lucas Block and the former Out-patients' entrance viewed from Smithfield, 1888. Surgery House is shown as a single storey.

Doctors on the steps of Lucas Block, c.1904. The two senior men, in top hats, are John Langton and Richard Gill.

Nurse N. Stewart in the operating theatre in Lucas Block, 1904.

A gardener at work outside Lucas Block, c.1910.

necessary because the 'Surgery', as it was then known, had become inadequate for the growing number of patients, and the examination rooms were too small. The entrance facing Smithfield, with its distinctive steps and columns, dates from that time, when the two small waiting rooms which then existed were rebuilt and extended to form a single large hall. This hall remained in use as the out-patient waiting area until 1907.

Abutting Lucas Block to the west, and also with a facade on Smithfield, is a small building known as Surgery House. It was constructed by Philip Hardwick as a single storey, the ground floor of the present Surgery House being substantially the original building of 1842. In the mid nineteenth century it was the residence of the 'Curator of the Surgery', but in 1889 the Governors approved a scheme for

the 'better superintendence of the Surgery and Out-patients Room', which were to be placed under the care of a Sister with nurses to assist her; the house occupied by the Curator of the Surgery was to 'be enlarged and used for the accommodation of the Surgery Sister' and the nurses. The upper floors of Surgery House date from the time of this enlargement.

The southern part of Lucas Block still remains largely as it was built, apart from internal refurbishment, and the addition of a top floor to house an ophthalmic ward in 1869. This part of the building has always provided ward accommodation: for surgical cases before 1930, for gynaecological patients from 1930 to 1939, and as children's wards since reopening in 1954 after wartime closure.

At the end of the block, near the East Wing, is what appears to be a small extension, but the ground floor of this structure is in fact part of Hardwick's original work of 1842. Until 1939 this was an operating theatre – the first purpose-built theatre in the Hospital. It was there in the early years of the twentieth century that Henry Gaskin Boyle first used the famous anaesthetic apparatus which bears his name. The theatre originally had semi-circular galleries from which students could view the operations, but these were later removed, and the theatre was remodelled in 1913 as a memorial to R.B. Etherington-Smith, a promising young surgeon who died of pneumococcal peritonitis at the age of 36. For many years after the Second World War the former theatre has housed the Department of Anaesthetics, but it still retains a number of its original features.

In the 1930s the former out-patient hall was used as the nurses' dining room, and since the 1950s it has housed the Physiotherapy Department. In the late 1980s and early 1990s substantial improvement work took place, beginning with the internal renovation of Surgery House in 1987 to provide residential accommodation for parents of child patients in Lucas and Kenton Wards. Between 1989 and 1991 Lucas Block itself underwent major restoration: the children's wards and the Physiotherapy Department were refurbished, a hydrotherapy pool and paediatric out-patients unit were constructed in the basement, the former ground floor entrance in Smithfield was rescued from dereliction, and the first and second floors above it were completely rebuilt.

LITTLE BRITAIN

The northern end of this street now seems almost part of the Hospital, but it has not always been so. The name 'Brettone Strete' can be traced back to the fourteenth century, and probably derives from a man named Robert le Bretoun who owned property in the vicinity. By the seventeenth century the name 'Little Britain' was well established; it then ran from St Botolph's church in Aldersgate Street, first in a westerly direction, then north for a short distance, and then west again, ending at the old Little Britain Gate of the Hospital. The street which divides the Hospital's original island site from Bartholomew Close was known as Duck Lane until about 1780 and as Duke Street from then until 1885.

Until early in the eighteenth century Duck Lane was famous for its bookshops and printers. In the 1660s Samuel Pepys made several visits there, on one occasion noting in his diary: 'To Duck Lane,

East side of Duke Street, 1880 (site now occupied by no. 38 Little Britain). The entrance to Bartholomew Close can be seen at the right.

Duke Street in 1807. The houses later used as Medical School accommodation are in the right background, and the site of the present Nurses' Gate in Little Britain is in the centre of the picture.

The Little Britain Gate, with a porter, 1911.

Little Britain, looking south, c.1929.

and there kissed the bookseller's wife...'. In 1725 Benjamin Franklin, later to become a renowned philosopher and statesman in America, was apprenticed to a printer whose workshop was in the church of St Bartholomew the Great. Franklin himself lived in lodgings in Little Britain for which he paid one shilling and sixpence per week.

In Victorian times the houses on the west side of what was then Duke Street were used as residential accommodation for students at the Medical School. James Paget, who later became Surgeon to the Hospital, lived there from 1843 to 1851, in the Warden's house; and it was there that Paget's wife suffered so greatly from hearing the cries of the patients in the operating theatre nearby, in the days before the introduction of anaesthetics.

During the nineteenth century the Little Britain Gate, previously located close to the southern end of the East Wing, was moved eastwards; and Duke Street was subsequently renamed as part of Little Britain. Photographs from the beginning of the twentieth century show that the Gate was then rather grander than it is now, with a porter's lodge,

two ornate metal gates providing an opening for vehicles, and smaller ones on either side for pedestrians. In 1925 the Little Britain Gate was moved once more, and was reconstructed on a more modest scale a little to the north of its former site. Since that time it has often been known as the Nurses' Gate. Some of the pillars and metal grilles from the old Gate were preserved and reused when the present goods entrance was opened in 1927 at the south-eastern extremity of the Hospital precinct. They continued in use until the 1960s when the goods entrance was widened and the old gates were removed. Of the original fittings, only the pillars now remain.

The area between the backs of the former Medical School houses and the rear of the East Wing was known as Well Yard, from a well which stood there in the eighteenth century. The houses were destroyed by enemy action in 1944, and in the 1960s the Hospital erected a temporary building on the site.

Bomb damage in Little Britain, 1940.

The Antony Brett Catering Block, named after a former Steward of the Hospital, was built there in 1989 and opened in 1990.

The east side of Little Britain was mainly occupied by tradesmen's workshops before the Second World War and was not generally used for Hospital purposes until the 1950s. In the late twentieth century this side of the street came to be dominated by the Queen Elizabeth II Wing and Gloucester House, both opened in 1961, and even more by the commercial office building erected by a private developer in 1991–2 when Montague Street was constructed immediately to the south of Gloucester House.

BARTHOLOMEW CLOSE

Now a winding street to the east of Little Britain, this name originally referred to the precinct of the priory of St Bartholomew. The priory was founded by Rahere in 1123 at the same time as the Hospital, and the chancel of the priory church still survives as the parish church of St Bartholomew the Great. Parts of the church were carefully restored in the late nineteenth century, but much of its superb Norman architecture remains largely unaltered since Rahere's lifetime. The area adjacent to the church was the place where, in the medieval period, the priory monks had their refectory, dormitory and other domestic buildings, the cloister where they worked and took their exercise, and their garden

The churchyard and west front of St Bartholomew the Great, 1737.

Bartholomew Close in 1844.

Bartholomew Close after an air raid in the Second World War, 1939–45.

and farm which supplied their produce. The priory was suppressed by King Henry VIII in 1539 and all its property seized. In 1544 it was granted to the courtier Richard Rich, who paid a little over £1000 for 'the capital messuage and mansion-house of the dissolved monastery or priory of St Bartholomew and that Close of the same' with all the buildings including 'the kitchen, the buttery, the pantry...and the prior's stable, situate within the Close'.

During the sixteenth and seventeenth centuries the Close was developed with the building of several town houses, one of which was owned by Walter Mildmay, Chancellor of the Exchequer under Queen Elizabeth I, whose exotic marble monument survives in St Bartholomew the Great. The poet John Milton lived in Bartholomew Close in 1660 and William Hogarth, whose magnificent paintings decorate the staircase leading to the Great Hall, was born there in 1697. During the eighteenth century the character of the Close changed with the building of many more tenements and shops linked by passageways and alleys, so that by the nineteenth century it was said to have provided Charles Dickens with the model for Fagin's kitchen in *Oliver Twist*.

A royal visit to the Hospital: Queen Elizabeth II in Bartholomew Close, 1961.

It was not until the 1920s that the Hospital began to acquire property in Bartholomew Close. In recent years the Close has housed numerous Hospital departments including Radiotherapy, Virology and Psychological Medicine, besides the St Bartholomew's Clinical Research Centre and the College of Nursing and Midwifery. Two notable older buildings are William Harvey House (formerly Middlesex House; renamed in 1966) and Dominion House. Both date from the 1870s. By the last decade of the twentieth century Bart's had acquired practically all of the western part of the Close with the exception of the Butchers' Hall.

Queen Elizabeth II Wing

This building, prominently sited between Little Britain and Bartholomew Close, was opened in 1961, but its origins can be traced back to the years of the Second World War. On the outbreak of war in 1939 many of the departments at Bart's, and their patients, had been rapidly evacuated to Hill End Hospital near St Albans, Hertfordshire. During the war there were sometimes as many as 800 Bart's patients in the wards at Hill End, but after 1945 general medical and surgical patients returned to the Hospital in Smithfield, and by 1953 only five specialist units remained in Hertfordshire. These were the Orthopaedic, E.N.T., Ophthalmic, Neurosurgical and Thoracic Departments, for which no accommodation was then available on the Smithfield site.

The planning of a new 'Special Departments' building began in 1950, and construction started in 1955. The chosen site was an area of about half an acre next to the church of St Bartholomew the Great, which had previously been occupied by bomb-damaged properties and trade workshops associated with Smithfield Market. Most of the building is in russet brown brick, but the main entrance bay is faced with Portland stone. The building was designed by the architects Adams, Holden and Pearson. In the planning stages it was called 'The L-shaped Block' because of its configuration along the south and west sides of the former cloister garth of St Bartholomew the Great, which was restored and preserved as an open space. The name now used for the building was selected to mark its formal opening by Queen Elizabeth II in May 1961.

The surgical specialities then returned from Hill End: the Orthopaedic Department moved into renovated wards on the ground floor of the West Wing, and the other units were accommodated in the Queen Elizabeth II Wing, which at that time also housed the Cardiology, Radiology and Isotope Departments.

Queen Elizabeth II Wing: exterior view, 1961.

A day room in the Queen Elizabeth II Wing, 1961.

In Henry Butlin Ward, Queen Elizabeth II Wing, 1961.

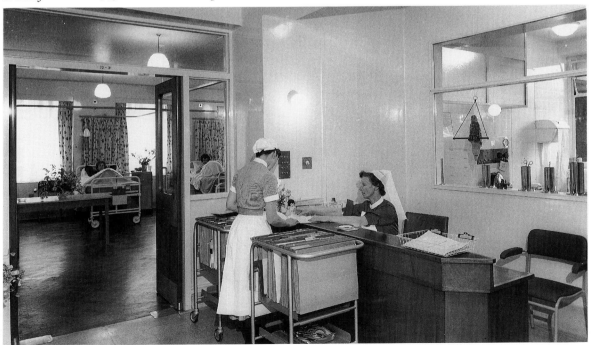

Queen Mary Wing and Gloucester House

Until the 1920s the Hospital had no purpose-built accommodation for nurses. Throughout the nineteenth century every Ward Sister lived and slept in a room next to her ward, but nurses below the rank of Sister were less fortunate. In the early part of the century a disused ward in the West Wing was employed as a nurses' dormitory, but by the 1860s many nurses found themselves obliged to sleep in cramped and windowless quarters scarcely larger than cupboards, which had been hastily constructed under the staircases of the main ward blocks. From the 1870s onwards a number of houses, chiefly in the vicinity of the Little Britain Gate, were converted into nurses' accommodation, and at the beginning of the twentieth century further rooms became available in an old building which the Governors purchased from Christ's Hospital.

Plans for a purpose-built nurses' home were made before the First World War, but the foundation stone was not laid until 1921 when Queen Mary, wife of King George V, visited the Hospital to perform the ceremony. The first part of the new

A Sister in her room, c.1905.

(Above): *Queen Mary's Nurses' Home, c.1929, seen from Well Yard.*

(Top right): *Building of extension to Queen Mary's Nurses' Home, c.1929.*

(Bottom right): *Gloucester House immediately after construction, 1961.*

(Below): *Nurses' study room in Queen Mary's Nurses' Home, c.1933.*

Four nurses reading in the Isla Stewart Library, c.1931.

Queen Mary's Nurses' Home in Little Britain was brought into use in October 1923. It had 160 rooms, each furnished with a bed, wardrobe and washstand; there were three bathrooms on each corridor. An extension was opened in 1926, and a further extension, with bedrooms for Sisters, in 1930. When new wards were opened in the same year they included a sitting room for each Sister but a bedroom on the ward was not provided. A library for nurses was erected in 1929 next to the Nurses' Home; it was named the Isla Stewart Memorial Library, in commemoration of the Matron whose house had once occupied the site.

After the Second World War a Matron's flat was fitted out on the first floor of the Nurses' Home. The main entrance to the Home was remodelled in 1968. By the 1970s the Hospital no longer had a resident Matron and the flat was then converted to office accommodation for the management of the City and Hackney Health District. By 1990 further parts of the building had come to be used as offices and in that year its name was changed to Queen Mary Wing.

The construction of further accommodation for nurses was approved by the Board of Governors in 1955, and a site was selected on the east side of Little Britain, opposite Queen Mary's Nurses' Home. The twelve-storey building was begun in 1958 and completed in 1961, when it was named Gloucester House in honour of the Duke of Gloucester, President of the Hospital. Besides bedrooms for nurses, it provided a recreation hall (Gloucester Hall), a swimming pool and purpose-built class and lecture rooms for the School of Nursing. An extension to Gloucester House, with substantially enlarged facilities for nurse education, was approved by the Governors in 1969 and opened in 1976.

Nurses' coffee bar, Gloucester House, 1961.

Gloucester House swimming pool, 1961.

King George V Block

This name is now applied to the whole complex of buildings occupying the site between the Square and the southern boundary of the Hospital. However it originally referred only to the part of the complex facing the Square, which was designed to accommodate the medical wards.

The story of the development of the site goes back to 1902, when Christ's Hospital School moved from the City of London to Horsham, Sussex. Since the sixteenth century Christ's Hospital had been the immediate neighbour of Bart's, occupying premises to the south of St Bartholomew's Hospital and extending as far as Newgate Street. When Christ's Hospital left the City the larger part of its site was acquired by the Post Office, but a small part was bought by St Bartholomew's. The buildings were

Former Christ's Hospital building, c.1927, on the site now occupied by the Surgical Block. Part of Queen Mary's Nurses' Home is visible in the background.

Surgical Block under construction, c.1929.

Surgical Block nearing completion, c.1929.

adapted as a temporary nurses' home. When the first purpose-built nurses' home was erected in the 1920s the former Christ's Hospital buildings were demolished and the Governors allocated most of the site for the construction of a new surgical block.

This block was built in 1928–9 on an alignment parallel to the southern boundary of the Hospital. It was designed to accommodate four surgical 'firms' and the Surgical Professorial Unit, and each of its five main floors was accordingly provided with two wards (one male, one female) and an operating theatre. Each unit occupied a complete floor. The architect was W.T.A. Lodge of the firm Lanchester and Lodge, and the block was opened in July 1930 by the Lord Mayor of London and Bishop H.L. Paget of Chester, the son of the distinguished surgeon James Paget.

The Governors then proceeded to plan the construction of a medical block to adjoin the new surgical building. The chosen site was at that time occupied by the South Wing of the Square, built in 1736–9 to the design of James Gibbs. Eighteenth century architecture was not then as highly valued as it is today, and a decision was made that the

South Wing should be demolished; from 1930 to 1934 it stood largely empty and in 1935 it was pulled down. The King George V Medical Block was then erected on the site, the name having been chosen by the King himself in 1934. It was opened in July 1937 by his widow, Queen Mary.

The Medical Block was also designed with five main floors, each with two wards; four floors were assigned to the four medical 'firms' and one to the Medical Professorial Unit. Once again the architect was W.T.A. Lodge. He aligned the main facade of the Medical Block with the buildings in the Square; and whereas the Surgical Block had only brick frontages, the north front of the Medical Block was faced with Portland stone to harmonise with the Gibbs buildings. At its rear the Medical Block abutted directly onto the Surgical Block, and direct communication between the two was provided, although the different alignments of the two buildings resulted in angular junctions between their respective floors. A peculiar feature of the Medical Block is that what appears to be the main entrance from the Square gives access only to steps leading down to the basement level.

After the Second World War the Medical and Surgical Blocks began to be perceived as one building, and the name 'King George V Block' came to be

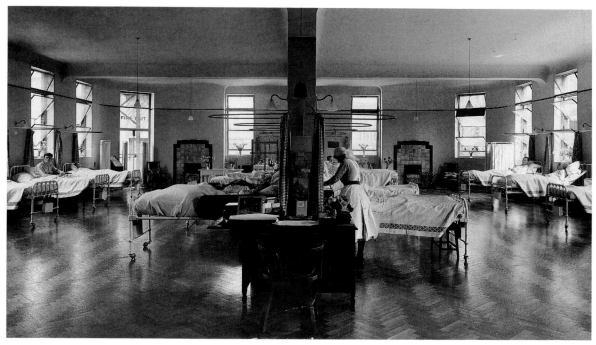

A ward in the King George V Medical Block, c.1937–8.

St. Bartholomew's Hospital
LONDON

✧

OPENING
OF THE
New Medical Block
"KING GEORGE V BUILDING"
by
Her Majesty Queen Mary
on
Thursday, the 8th July, 1937, at 3 p.m.

used to describe both parts. Extensions to the block, including a Central Sterile Supplies Department, were made in the 1960s. The distinction between the medical and surgical parts of the block was rigidly maintained until 1980, when the Henry Butlin Ear Nose and Throat Unit was opened in what had previously been medical ward accommodation. New operating and sterilizing departments were constructed in the basement between 1990 and 1992, and a new colonnaded entrance to the whole block was provided in 1991 on the former site of the Cohen Garden for Nurses.

King George V Medical Block commemorative brochure, 1937.

THE GILTSPUR STREET BUILDINGS

Giltspur Street was traditionally said to derive its name from the spurs worn by medieval knights who rode to joust in Smithfield; or possibly a gilt spur may have been the trade sign of a spurrier who worked there. Giltspur Street now runs from Newgate Street to meet Smithfield at the far end of the Library and Museum Block, but until the 1870s the dividing point between the two streets was at the Hartshorn Gate, which gave access to the Hospital at the rear of the West Wing. Vehicles approaching from Giltspur Street or Smithfield came into the

Hospital through this entrance as in the mid nineteenth century the Henry VIII Gate was used only by pedestrians. The approach to the Hartshorn Gate on the Hospital side was known as Tart's Court, and part of its route can still be followed along the pathway which runs between the West Wing and the new Pathology Building of 1971, leading to a cul-de-sac outside the Library windows.

In 1877 the Hartshorn Gate was demolished and the Library and Museum Block was constructed on the site in 1878–9. This block is the oldest of the

The Hartshorn Gate, with adjoining buildings in West Smithfield and Giltspur Street, c.1876. The entrance to Windmill Court is at the right of the photograph.

Exterior of the Library and Museum Block, 1879.

existing structures along this part of the Hospital's frontage. The exterior of the building is in an Italianate style faced with Portland stone; the architect was Edward I'Anson.

Immediately to the south-west of the Library and Museum Block was Windmill Court. In the eighteenth century this was a lane which formed the boundary of the Hospital and extended for a considerable distance approximately parallel to the rear of the West Wing. By the middle of the nineteenth century, however, Windmill Court had become a short cul-de-sac, as the dissecting rooms and lecture theatres of the expanding Medical School were built along its former course. In 1988 a Resuscitation Unit was built on the last remaining part of Windmill Court, which therefore no longer exists as a public thoroughfare, although its street sign can still be seen on the Hospital facade.

Beyond the site of Windmill Court stands the imposing frontage of the Out-patients Building and resident staff quarters. The foundation stone of this building was laid in 1904 by King Edward VII; the text on the stone recalls the benevolence of King Henry I at the Hospital's foundation in 1123, and its sonorously correct phrasing was the work of the physician Norman Moore, author of a monumental history of the Hospital. The building, completed in 1907, was designed by Edward Blakeway I'Anson, who had succeeded his father as Surveyor to the Hospital in 1888. It is evidently meant to be viewed from the opposite side of Giltspur Street, whence the formal stonework is seen to advantage; the southern facade, visible when approaching from Newgate Street, is dull by comparison. The ground floor of the building is approximately one metre above the level of Giltspur Street, and for many years this meant that stretcher cases had to be lifted up a small flight of stairs. However the entrance vestibule was redesigned in 1964, and more extensively in 1990 when a retail shop was opened there.

The last of the major buildings to be erected to the south-west of the Henry VIII Gate was the Pathological Block of 1907–9, also designed by E.B. I'Anson. The old houses on the site were demolished in 1907; they had been leased to shopkeepers and were the last part of the Hospital's frontage to be let to

Giltspur Street, looking south, 1904. This drawing was made before demolition work began for the construction of the Out-patients Building.

Giltspur Street, c.1910, after construction of new buildings.

An ambulance casualty in the entrance court of the Out-patients Building, c.1929.

tenants. Another stone inscription composed by Norman Moore records that the site was once occupied by the house of Joanna Astley, nurse to King Henry VI in the fifteenth century. After the construction of this block the Hospital frontage remained unaltered until 1971, when the new Pathology Building was given a small frontage on Giltspur Street which filled the gap between the older structures in a rather unsympathetic style.

CHARTERHOUSE SQUARE

The site in Charterhouse Square occupied by the Medical College of St Bartholomew's Hospital was acquired by the College in 1933–4. By a coincidence of history, however, part of the site had belonged to the Hospital in its very earliest days; it was sold in 1370 and passed through various hands before reverting to Bart's after an interval of almost six centuries.

In the 1340s the Hospital possessed a piece of land called Spital Croft, which Sir Walter de Manny, a distinguished soldier and courtier, converted to a burial ground for victims of the Black Death, the terrible plague which ravaged England in the reign of King Edward III. In 1370 the Hospital sold the land to de Manny, who founded the monastery of the Charterhouse there in the following year. The monastery was dissolved in 1537–8 and in 1611 the site was bought by Thomas Sutton, who had made his fortune from coal mining on Tyneside. Sutton established a charitable foundation comprising a school and an almshouse. A few parts of the monastic structures survived to be adapted for Sutton's Charterhouse, which still exists within its ancient buildings as a home for gentlemen pensioners. Charterhouse School became one of England's most famous public schools, and moved to Godalming in

The Charterhouse in the eighteenth century.

A drawing of the site in Charterhouse Square, 1933, showing buildings acquired from the Merchant Taylors' School.

The Physics Block, Charterhouse Square, after air raid damage, 1941.

1872. The part of the site formerly occupied by the school was then sold to the Merchant Taylors' Company, which also used it for educational purposes, and erected a number of new buildings in the Victorian Gothic style. The Merchant Taylors' School functioned there until 1933 when it too moved to the country.

The Medical College of St Bartholomew's Hospital then bought the school site with the intention of using it to house its pre-clinical departments and as student accommodation. Some of the Merchant Taylors' buildings were adapted and new ones were built. The Departments of Chemistry, Biochemistry, Physics, Physiology and Pharmacology moved to Charterhouse Square in 1935; Anatomy and Biology followed in 1936. Within five years, however, the site had been devastated by German air raids in the Second World War. In 1940 and 1941 about half of the buildings were destroyed and many of the others badly damaged.

In the post-war years new buildings were erected. Accommodation for students, which had been planned but not built before the war, received priority. College Hall was constructed between 1949 and 1952 to house 100 students; after its extension in 1966, 200 students could be accommodated. A Science Block on the northern and western sides of the College's site was built in progressive stages between 1952 and 1963.

In 1990 the pre-clinical departments were transferred to Queen Mary and Westfield College, Mile End. The former Anatomy building was then occupied by the Charterhouse College of Radiography. The Biochemistry teaching laboratory was demolished and replaced by the newly-built Wolfson Institute of Preventive Medicine, opened in 1992. The Institute was named to commemorate a donation from the Wolfson Foundation which met a large part of the building costs. Other areas have been used to accommodate new research groups

The Charterhouse, seen from the Medical College site, c.1977.

including the William Harvey Research Institute.

Despite the wartime destruction, two doorways of monks' cells from the Charterhouse monastery still exist on the Medical College site; one is in the eastern boundary wall and the other in the College of Radiography. The grass quadrangle still follows the approximate outline of the Great Cloister Garth of the monastery.

The former headmaster's house of the Merchant Taylors' School, built in 1894, also survived the war. The emblems of the Merchant Taylors' Company were carved on the facade of the building and can still be seen. Part of the house was used as a residence for the Warden of the College until 1973 and for the Dean from 1974 to 1989. In 1991 it was refurnished as a venue for College meetings and hospitality.

Physicians and Surgeons:
The Medical Staff

Improbable as it may seem to those who know the Hospital today, there were no medical staff employed at Bart's for the first four hundred years of its existence. Some medical men may have visited the Hospital, but patients in the middle ages were under the care of the Master, Brethren and Sisters of the Hospital, who were members of a religious order. It was King Henry VIII's charter which first required the Hospital to employ 'one person sufficiently learned in the science of physic, and one other person having sufficient knowledge in surgery'. In the event, several surgeons were appointed. The first whose names are recorded, in 1547–8, were Mr Martyn, Richard Westall, George Vaughan, Thomas Bayley and William Gartar. In 1548 Gartar received a number of special payments for curing patients; the Governors paid him at the rate of five shillings apiece, and among his patients were Francis Hall 'that was burnt with gunpowther', Margery Coke 'being a year and a half sick', and Agnes Charwarde who had been bitten by a dog. A surgeon of greater distinction associated with St Bartholomew's at that time was Thomas Vicary, the first Master of the Barber-Surgeons' Company; Vicary is known to have been actively involved in the management of the Hospital, although there is no reliable evidence that he practised surgery within its walls.

Despite King Henry's injunction Bart's does not seem to have appointed a Physician until the 1560s, when the office was held by Roderigo Lopez (or Lopus). It was an inauspicious beginning, for Lopez was subsequently implicated in a plot to poison Queen Elizabeth I, and his life ended on the gallows. Timothy Bright, the inventor of shorthand, lived within the Hospital precinct and held the post of Physician from 1585 to 1592, but was dismissed for neglect of duty. However an appointment made by the Governors in the autumn of 1609 marked the beginning of a different era. One of the greatest names in medical history, William Harvey, the discoverer of the circulation of the blood, held office as

William Harvey. Eighteenth century copy of an original portrait attributed to William van Bemmel.

Physician to the Hospital from 1609 to 1643. His instructions required him to attend in the Hospital on at least one day a week throughout the year, to prescribe for such patients 'as shall need the counsel and advice of the Physician'. Like his predecessors, Harvey took up his appointment as the sole Physician on the staff of the Hospital. Not until the 1630s was an Assistant Physician's post established. By the end of the seventeenth century this post had been changed to that of a second full Physician, and a third Physician was appointed in 1750.

Only a few of the Hospital's Physicians of this period have left a lasting reputation. Anthony Askew, in office from 1754 to 1774, was better known for his hospitality and his prominent place

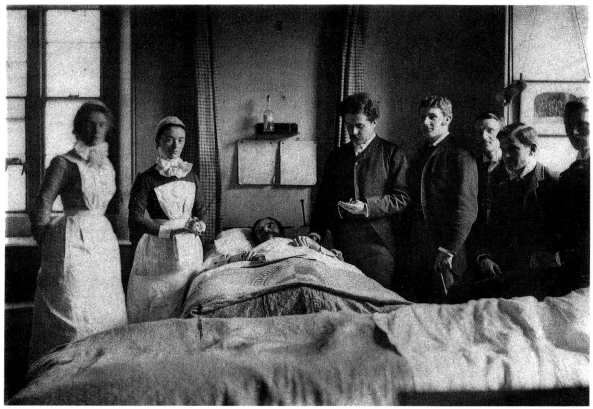

Archibald Garrod as a junior doctor at work on a ward, c.1885. Four medical students at right.

in London society than for his medical skills. The most noted Physicians at Bart's at this time were probably William Pitcairn, appointed in 1750, who maintained five acres of botanical gardens at his house in Islington; and his nephew and successor David Pitcairn, Physician from 1780 to 1793, who is credited with the first recognition of a connection between rheumatic fever and heart disease.

From 1547 onwards the Hospital generally had a staff of three or more Surgeons. Among the earliest were some notable names: William Clowes (Surgeon 1575–86), a prolific writer; John Woodall (1616–43), a pioneer of improved amputation techniques and author of *The Surgeon's Mate*; and John Freke, the first curator of the Pathological Museum at the Hospital. Freke became Assistant Surgeon in May 1725 and full Surgeon four years later. In 1727, as Assistant Surgeon, he had been asked by the Governors 'through a tender regard for the deplorable state of blind people…to couch and take care of the diseases of the eyes of such poor persons as shall be thought by him fit for the operation'. However this early instance of specialisation did not

establish a precedent, and Freke's successors were all generalists. Among these the most distinguished names were Percival Pott, Surgeon from 1749 to 1787, noted for the fracture which bears his name and which he himself suffered by falling from his horse; and John Abernethy, Surgeon from 1815 to 1827, the greatest lecturer of his day, who first established the reputation of the Medical School at Bart's.

Men such as Pott and Abernethy were followed by large numbers of pupils and dressers, who helped with their hospital work in return for the opportunity to learn from the experience of the great men. But the Hospital did not yet offer a full career structure for those who wished to enter the world of medicine. Dresserships were only available to those who could pay for the privilege. Resident house surgeons were first appointed in the late eighteenth century, and their posts were formally established on a salaried basis in 1813, but they were very few in number; and there were no house physicians until 1868. Later in the century, however, the fees for dresserships were abolished and a number of additional posts became available for qualified men as the Hospital increased its staff to cope with the growing numbers of patients.

In 1854 fourth posts of full Physician and Surgeon were created. The number of Surgeons was again increased, from four to five, in 1882; and a fifth Physician's post was established in 1895. The complement of house surgeons was changed from four to ten in 1882. By the end of the nineteenth century the system of 'firms' had come into being. In 1900 there were five medical and five surgical firms, all with their own wards. A firm was headed by one of the Physicians or Surgeons, and his deputy was one of the Assistant Physicians or Assistant Surgeons. Every firm also had two house officers, each serving for twelve months only (six months as junior houseman and six as senior), who were responsible for the care of the patients between the visits of the senior staff. Medical students were also attached to the firm as dressers or clinical clerks. In the twentieth century each firm acquired an additional post of Chief Assistant (subsequently known as Senior

Registrar), and later still a Junior Registrar's post was added. The firms came to be known by the names of colours; traditionally the Orange, Scarlet, Purple, Silver and Gold firms have been medical firms, and the Dark Blue, Light Blue, Green, Pink and Yellow firms have been surgical.

The Victorian age was also an era of increasing specialisation. George Burrows, Physician 1841–64, had specialised in forensic medicine in the earlier part of his career. Frederic John Farre, Physician 1854–69, specialised in botany and materia medica; William Lawrence, Surgeon 1824–65, is now recognised as one of the founders of British ophthalmology; Edward Stanley, Surgeon 1838–61, was noted for his extensive knowledge of bone disease. However apart from lectureships none of these men had specialist appointments. All were general Physicians or Surgeons to the Hospital; as was the greatest clinician at Bart's in the nineteenth century, James Paget, who held the post of Surgeon from 1861 to 1871. Although the Hospital's first dental surgeon was appointed in 1837, and the first

Henry Butlin, Surgeon, with his firm, c.1894–5. Butlin is seated centre right, holding his top hat.

W. Bruce Clarke's firm, 1904. Bruce Clarke in top hat; senior house surgeon wearing white coat.

accoucheur (gynaecologist) in 1848, no further specialist appointments were made for another twenty years. Only in the latter part of the century did the Hospital begin to establish special departments where expertise in a particular field could be developed and employed to full use. The first appears to have been the Eye Department, established in 1869 when an ophthalmic ward was built in what is now Lucas Block. At a meeting of the Governors later in the same year the Hospital recognised that it was no longer possible to expect all its senior staff to practise every branch of their art, and thereafter specialist departments were set up in orthopaedics, dermatology, ear and throat surgery, and later in other specialities also. In many cases, however, no beds were assigned, and the departments were restricted to out-patient treatment, the head of the department commonly having only the status of an Assistant Physician or Assistant Surgeon.

Not everyone who achieved high office in the Hospital was in the front line of advancing medical

knowledge. William Savory, Surgeon 1867–91, and George William Callendar, Surgeon 1871–9, were vehemently opposed to Joseph Lister's views on infection, and Lister's antiseptic techniques were not brought into full use at Bart's until after Callendar's death in 1879.

In the late nineteenth, and more especially in the twentieth century, the numbers of medical staff continued to expand. In 1890 the list of 'Medical and Surgical Staff' contained 39 names; one hundred years later there were more than 200 consultants and honorary consultants. Out of so many it is not easy to select a few for mention; but among many others the staff of the Hospital has included Samuel Gee, Physician 1878–1904, noted for his aphorisms and his paper 'On the Coeliac Affection'; Henry Butlin, Surgeon 1892–1902, who won a substantial reputation on diseases of the throat and tongue; Thomas Lauder Brunton, Physician 1895–1904, pioneer of the use of amyl nitrate in treating angina pectoris; and Holburt Waring, Surgeon 1909–31,

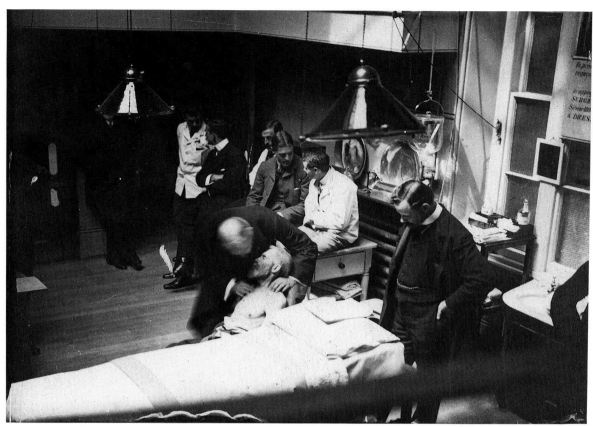

Examining a patient, c.1905.

distinguished for his contribution to medical education and his work on diseases of the liver. In 1919 one medical and one surgical firm were each converted into a Professorial Unit established in association with the University of London. A number of the Hospital's most notable figures were to hold these professorships, including Archibald Garrod, Professor of Medicine 1919–20, Francis Fraser, Professor of Medicine 1921–34, and James Paterson Ross, Professor of Surgery 1935–60. Others who have worked at Bart's include Thomas Dunhill, noted for his work in thyroid surgery in the 1920s; Thomas Horder, the most distinguished physician in England in the 1930s and subsequently a leading opponent of the National Health Service; Archibald McIndoe, famous for his remarkable feats of plastic surgery during the Second World War; Geoffrey Keynes, whose contributions to surgical knowledge were matched by his expertise in literary bibliography; and Gordon Hamilton Fairley, the noted cancer specialist who was killed by a terrorist bomb in 1975.

Two doctors in the Square, c.1905. Norman Moore, Physician, has his back to the photographer; Howard Marsh, Surgeon, is facing the camera.

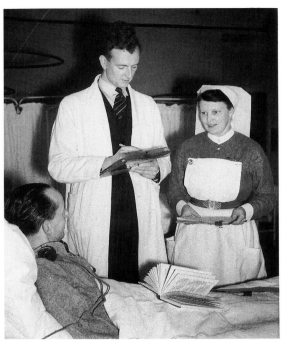

A doctor at work, c.1950. This photograph was taken in Fleet Street Ward.

Traditionalists at St Bartholomew's were long reluctant to adopt the term 'consultant', and it was not used officially until after the National Health Service was established in 1948. In the earlier part of the century the senior doctors were those 'on the Staff', a position formally denied to their junior colleagues. When this designation was felt to be untenable, the term 'visiting staff' was used to distinguish the senior men. Each member of this elite held a post as Physician, Surgeon, Assistant Physician or Assistant Surgeon to the Hospital. After Bart's was absorbed into the NHS the titles of Assistant Physician and Assistant Surgeon were abolished, and all the postholders were promoted to the rank of Physician or Surgeon, though a distinction remained between those who were in charge of a firm or department, and those who were not.

Throughout the second half of the twentieth century the number of specialist posts and departments increased, and the number of beds assigned to the firms in general medicine and surgery was accordingly eroded. The growth of specialism led to the introduction of new job titles, and senior staff were appointed as Consultant Neurologist, Consultant Cardiologist, etc.; similar titles were used in each speciality. These changes also led to the abandonment of the traditional titles of Physician and Surgeon to the Hospital. By the 1960s the remaining generalists had become Consultant Physicians and Consultant Surgeons. After the NHS reorganisation of 1974, posts were established with responsibilities in one or more of the Hackney hospitals as well as at Bart's.

In 1990 the Hospital's management structure was radically revised in accordance with the current NHS practice, and clinical directorates were introduced, each with a senior consultant at its head, to manage the provision of clinical services on the Hackney and Homerton sites as well as at Smithfield. Of the twenty directorates, only four were given generalist titles. General surgery was reorganised into three firms which formed part of the 'Surgery A' directorate, while 'Surgery B' covered ophthalmology, oral, plastic, and ear, nose and throat surgery. The two general medical directorates (amalgamated in 1992) provided services in endocrinology, genito-urinary medicine, respiratory medicine, dermatology and gastroenterology as well as general medicine. The remaining directorates covered the whole range of specialisation, including separate directorates established for cardiac services, neurosciences, cancer services, renal medicine, urology, and trauma and locomotor disorders.

Operations and Operating Theatres

The first known surgical operations at Bart's were performed in the 1540s. In 1547 Mr Martyn, a surgeon, was paid ten shillings 'for cutting of a boy of the stone'. Apart from amputations, lithotomy, or cutting of the stone, was the only operation commonly performed in the Hospital in the late sixteenth and seventeenth centuries. An order of 1654 required that the Governors should be given advance notice of any lithotomy so that those who wished could view the operation; a further order in 1672 stated that patients should not be admitted more than 'two days and two nights...before they be cut'; and in 1714 it was laid down 'that the stones taken out of the patients' bladders...be brought into the Counting House and showed to the Governors at their next meeting...and hung up in the said Counting House according to ancient custom'.

Patients awaiting lithotomies were accommodated in a ward known as the Cutting Ward, and it was there that the operations took place. In 1691 Sir William Prichard, President of the Hospital, gave £2000 for a new Cutting Ward, and the building was

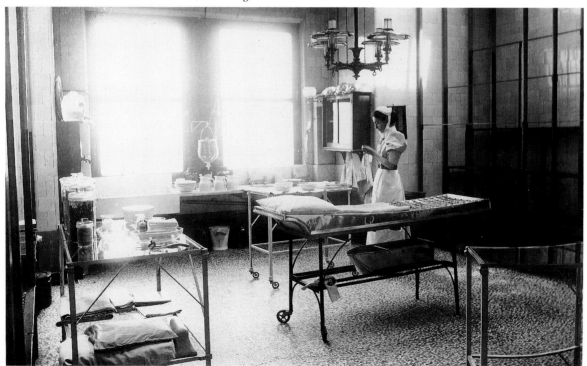

The New Theatre (later known as Theatre B), East Wing, 1899.

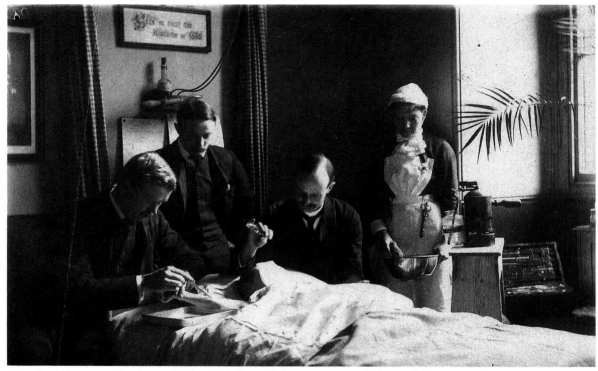

Anaesthesia for an operation in a ward bed, c.1890. Surgeon's instrument case and Lister carbolic spray at right of photograph.

finished by 1693. It stood in the Long Walk, a little to the south of the present site of the West Wing. In 1722 the Governors ordered the building of a skylight in the roof over the cutting table, 'for casting of a better light to the place that operation is performed in'. At the same time a rail for spectators was fitted, 'for keeping off the press of the company upon the surgeons when they are cutting'.

The Cutting Ward was closed in 1769 and the patients were moved into the newly-built East Wing, where two wards had been set aside for surgical cases. A theatre had also been constructed in the East Wing following a Governors' order of May 1766, and it continued in use until the 1840s. An operation, however, was performed only rarely; in pre-anaesthetic days it was a terrible ordeal for the patient, and surgeons such as John Abernethy disliked operating except in cases of dire necessity. In the 1770s the number of operations averaged between 55 and 60 a year, while the Governors' minutes for 1814 give the annual number at that time as about 72.

In 1842 a new purpose-built operating theatre was constructed at the south end of the new Casualty Block (now called Lucas Block). From 1842 until the 1890s this was the only operating theatre in the

Hospital. Operations were still relatively infrequent (fewer than 500 a year in the mid nineteenth century), and convention required that only a senior surgeon might perform them. The allotted day for operations was Saturday, and only in a rare emergency were they performed on other days of the week. By March 1847 ether was in use at Bart's, only a few months after its first use as an anaesthetic in the United States. Anaesthesia by chloroform was introduced later in the same year. The first operations under anaesthetic took place in the Lucas Block theatre, although the practice of performing minor operations in the wards persisted until the early twentieth century.

A nurse who worked in this theatre in the 1890s recalled that it then 'still contained the table on which formerly the patients were strapped for operation, before the use of anaesthetics; [but] it was only used then as the nurses' table...The cupboards were antiquated; there was one containing sand, and when the surgeon felt the floor getting sticky, he called for this, and the nurse took a shovelful from the cupboard and spread it on the floor. Another cupboard contained hooks, above which were painted the names of well-known surgeons, and on those hooks used to hang their discarded

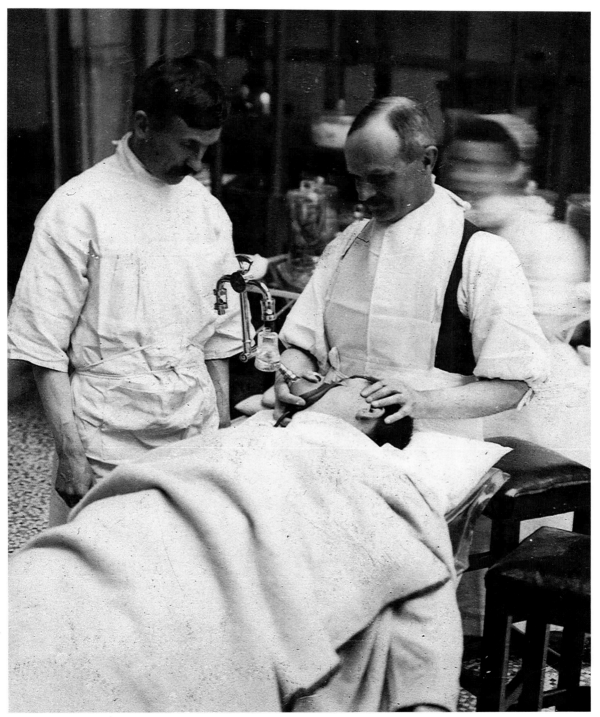

Charles Hadfield and Edgar Willett administering anaesthetic in Theatre B, c.1905.

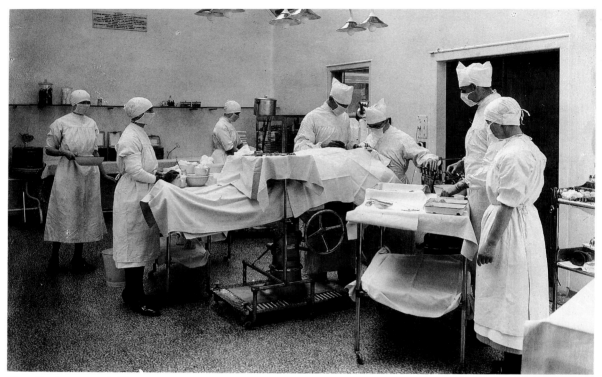

Operation in progress in Theatre A, c.1929.

E.N.T. operation, c.1929.

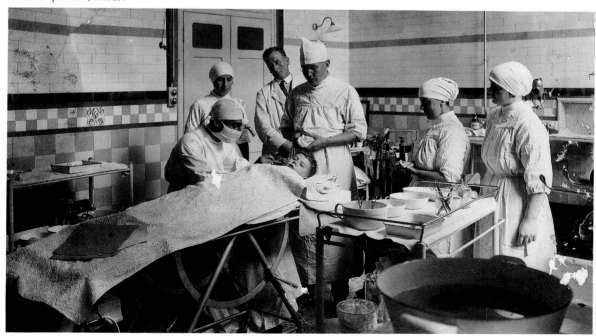

society frock-coats, only now fit for operating in!'. She remembered being told 'how proud Sir James Paget was of his [old frock-coat] when it became mahogany colour'. According to tradition these old coats became so stiff with blood that they could stand by themselves. By the 1880s the frock-coats had been abandoned, but surgical gowns were still unknown. The practice of operating in everyday clothes, wearing a linen apron but without gloves or masks, continued into the early years of the twentieth century.

Nevertheless improvements in surgical and anaesthetic practice had led to an increase in the number of operations that were performed: over 2000 a year in the 1890s, with a greatly reduced mortality. In 1894 a theatre was opened in the East Wing; this became known as the New Theatre and its counterpart in Lucas Block became the Old Theatre. By the beginning of the First World War, Bart's had seven theatres. The Old Theatre had been named Theatre A, and the New was known as Theatre B. From 1905 to 1930 Theatres C and D were in a lean-to building adjoining the east end of the North Wing. There were also Martha Theatre (a gynaecological theatre, closed in 1930) in the South Wing, Coborn Theatre (closed c.1939) in the West Wing, and an ophthalmic theatre, originally in Lucas Block but later rehoused in the East Wing.

Five new theatres were included in the Surgical Block opened in 1930. These were lettered alphabetically from C to G. Each adjoined a pair of surgical wards on the same floor. Theatre H for orthopaedic and ear, nose and throat surgery was opened in 1931 in the East Wing; it too was close to the wards assigned to these specialities. The intention was to reduce the movement of patients to a minimum, and in particular to avoid having to wheel operative cases out of doors. To a large extent this was achieved, but even in the 1980s patients in the West Wing wards faced a journey across the Square for their operations.

After the Second World War further theatres were opened: Theatre J in the East Wing in 1950; a new Theatre A, in an extension attached to the East Wing, in 1955; and a number of specialist theatres in the Queen Elizabeth II Wing in 1961. In the basement of the King George V Block an endoscopy theatre was opened in 1966, and a new suite of seven operating theatres was constructed between 1990 and 1992. By the beginning of the 1990s improved anaesthetic techniques and the development of minimally invasive 'keyhole' surgery meant that many operations no longer required an overnight stay in hospital; and in 1991 a Day Surgery Centre was opened in the East Wing, where operations could be completed and the patient sent home on the same day.

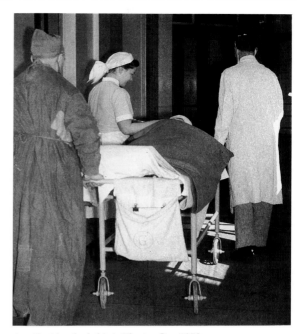

A patient is wheeled into Theatre G, c.1950.

Suturing; a drawing by Gary Jeffrey, 1987.

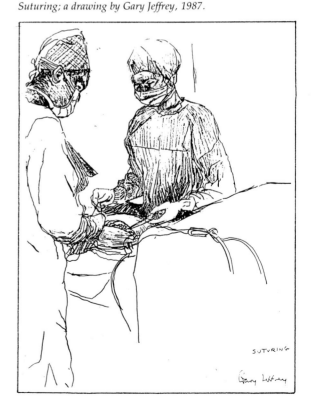

THE ELECTRICAL AND X-RAY DEPARTMENTS

Electrical treatment was first used in the Hospital in the late eighteenth century. In February 1777 the Governors ordered the purchase of an electrical machine, which apparently remained in use for some forty years. A print dated 1799, which was formerly hung in the Electrical Department at St Bartholomew's, shows the administration of elec-

tricity to a patient. By the middle of the nineteenth century, however, the electrical machinery had been abandoned. In 1912 William Church wrote in the *St Bartholomew's Hospital Journal* that when he first came to Bart's in the 1860s the electrical facilities 'consisted of two batteries kept in the Surgery for the purpose of stirring up drunks and persons

A young patient being treated by electrical machine, 1799. This print hung for many years on the wall of the former Electrical Department at Bart's.

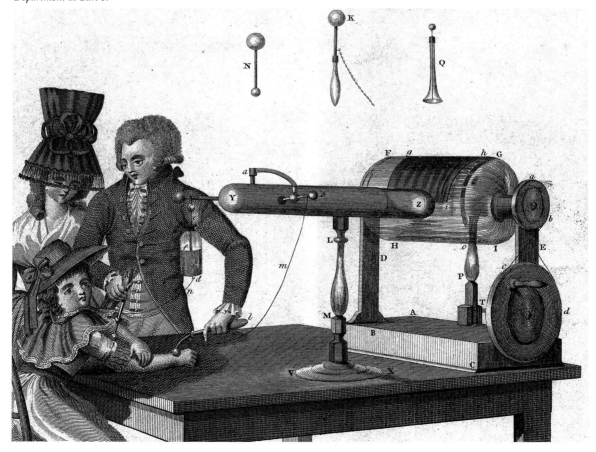

supposed to be suffering from opium poisoning'.

An Electrical Department was established in 1882 under W.E. Steavenson. Electricity was used both for diagnostic purposes and for treatment; 55 patients passed through the Department in its first year. After the discovery of X-rays in 1895, the Electrical Department also assumed responsibility for radiology at Bart's. Steavenson's successor, Henry Lewis Jones, took the first skiagram at the Hospital in April 1896, and the regular use of X-ray apparatus began in June of that year.

The X-ray Department was separated from the Electrical Department in 1912, and was itself later divided into Departments of Radiotherapy and Diagnostic Radiology. In the early days most of the work was diagnostic. Radiotherapy effectively began with the appointment of N.S. Finzi as Chief Assistant in 1913; Finzi achieved some remarkable results with high-voltage X-ray treatment of malignant growths, which led to the opening of the Mozelle Sassoon 'Million Volt' Unit in 1936. St Bartholomew's was thus the first hospital in Europe to enter the field of 'super-voltage' therapy. The pioneering work of Finzi, and his colleagues and successors, showed that higher voltage installations could provide far more effective treatment than was previously available, and in the 1950s a 15-million volt linear accelerator was acquired. In 1961 a new

X-ray apparatus at St Bartholomew's Hospital, c.1910.

Two patients in the Electrical Department, c.1929.

Radiologist examining X-rays, c.1929.

Radiotherapy, c.1929.

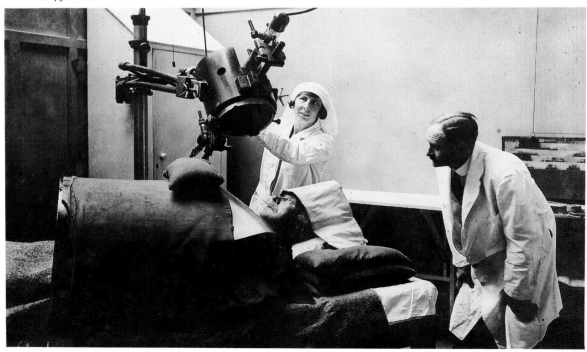

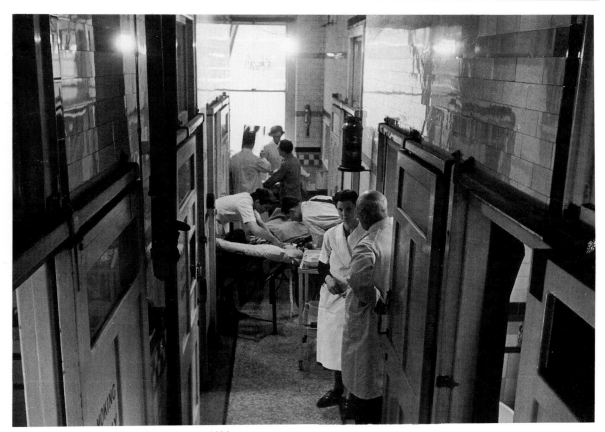

Staff at work in the Radiology Department, c.1938.

Radiotherapy Building was opened in Bartholomew Close, and linear accelerators of yet more advanced design were installed in the 1980s. In 1990 the Radiotherapy Department became part of the Directorate of Cancer Services, while Radiology became a Directorate in itself, providing a variety of services both at Homerton and on the Smithfield site.

A Radiographic Training Centre was established at Bart's in 1948 and became a regional training school in 1991, under the title of the Charterhouse College of Radiography.

Apothecaries, Dispensers and Pharmacists

The Pharmacy is one of the oldest-established parts of the Hospital and can trace its origins back to the sixteenth century when the first Apothecaries were employed to prepare drugs and medicines for the patients. The earliest whose name we know was William Weston, first mentioned in 1571–2. The most notable was Francis Bernard, who held office from 1661 to 1678. When the plague broke out in London in 1665, the Physicians fled from the city, but Bernard remained at his post and was authorised by the Governors to prescribe for the patients while the doctors were absent.

A 'shop', or workshop, for the Apothecary was opened in the Cloisters in 1614, and was fitted out with 'a great brass mortar', two iron pestles and a large quantity of other equipment. When it was demolished during the reconstruction of the Hospital in the eighteenth century, a new shop was established in the former Peter Ward at the rear of the site where the West Wing was to be built. After many more alterations and rebuildings, the Pharmacy today is still located behind the southern end of the

The Apothecary's shop, 1899.

Patients collecting medicines at the Dispensary counter, c.1929.

West Wing, having moved only a short distance since the 1740s.

In 1678 Francis Bernard was appointed Assistant Physician to the Hospital. Some of his ward books, in which he noted the medicines he gave to his patients, are preserved in the British Library. They indicate the kind of preparations made up in the Apothecary's shop at that time. For James Shallow, a patient in Long Ward in November 1679, Bernard prescribed *decoctum album*, which was made of hartshorn, cinnamon and coriander seed in water. John Bootland, another patient in the same ward, was given *aqua liberans*, consisting of guaiacum, liquorice root and lime-water.

Successive Apothecaries seem to have worked without any skilled help until 1797, when an assistant was appointed; thereafter the Apothecary's shop developed into a small department with a number of staff working under the Apothecary. On the death of Philip Hurlock, Apothecary from 1835 to 1847, his successor Frederick Wood was appointed as a kind of resident medical officer. He was not only to have charge of the Apothecary's shop, but was also to attend to medical casualties and to see in-patients when necessary in the absence of the Physicians. After Wood's retirement in 1868 the title of 'Apothecary' was discontinued

and his duties were divided between the new posts of House Physician and Dispenser (the latter taking over all pharmaceutical duties).

The name 'Apothecary's shop', however, remained in use until 1906–7 when the premises were rebuilt and renamed as the 'Dispensary'. At that time the Dispensary waiting hall could accommodate 250 people and included a kiosk where outpatients might obtain a bottle for their prescription if they had failed to bring a suitable container of their own. The title of Head Dispenser was changed to Pharmacist in 1927. Gradually the Pharmacist and his staff became more involved in drug applications and control, with dispensing being only one part of their activity. However the department continued to be known as the Dispensary until the 1960s, when the use of the term 'Pharmacy' became standard.

A number of objects from the old Apothecary's shop, including drug bottles, pill containers and three large copper measuring jugs, are preserved and displayed in the Pharmacy.

(Overleaf): *The Dispensary waiting hall, c.1923–5, with kiosk for bottles at right.*

Men at work in the Dispensary, c.1929.

NURSES

The first reference to a 'nurse' in the records of St Bartholomew's Hospital is found in the 1650s. The title of 'Sister', however, is much older. In the earliest centuries of the Hospital's existence its head was known as the Master and his staff were the Brethren and Sisters of the Hospital. They all took monastic vows as members of the Augustinian order and dedicated their lives to religious observance. It seems that there were generally four Sisters at St Bartholomew's in the years before the Reformation, and that their chief task was to attend and feed the patients.

In the 1540s the old order was swept away and the monastic life abolished. In the reformed Hospital, under the terms of the charter granted by King Henry VIII, there were to be 'one Matron and twelve women under her to make the beds and wash and attend upon' the patients. The first known Matron was Rose Fisher, whose name appears in the Hospital archives from 1547 to 1559; and the 'twelve women under her' assumed the title of 'Sister' which had been used by their medieval predecessors. The duties of the Sisters were set out in the Hospital's Order Book, published in 1552:

> 'Your charge is in all things to declare and show yourselves gentle, diligent, and obedient to the Matron of this house...ye shall also faithfully and charitably serve and help the poor [patients] in all their griefs and diseases, as well by keeping them sweet and clean, as in giving them their meats and drinks, after the most honest and comfortable manner; also ye shall use unto them good and honest talk, such as may comfort and amend them...'

In the late sixteenth century the Sisters wore a blue uniform and each had charge of one of the wards of the Hospital. Besides looking after the patients she fetched coal and provisions, emptied the slops, and did what she could to keep her ward clean. The Sisters washed all the patients' personal and bed linen by pounding it in a large wooden vat known as the Buck. They supplied their own wood-ash (soap was not used until 1687), and every sheet had to be accounted for to the Matron. Each Sister was responsible for the sheets used in her own ward and for drying, pressing and mending them.

Sister Lucas; an undated photograph, probably from the 1880s.

Two Sisters seated at tea table, c.1905. This photograph was taken in a courtyard on the site now occupied by the King George V Block.

Two nurses at work, c.1905. The ward is unidentified.

Formal group outside the South Wing, 1906. Assistant Matron in centre.

Nurses watching the arrival of royal visitors, 1921; a photograph taken on the occasion of the foundation stone ceremony for Queen Mary's Nurses' Home.

Until the middle of the seventeenth century she worked alone, with no staff to assist her. Helpers for the Sisters are first mentioned in 1647, and from the 1650s onwards these helpers were often called 'nurses'. In 1652 a rule was introduced, although not always observed in practice, that no Sister should be employed who did not have previous experience as a nurse or helper.

Some of the early Matrons of St Bartholomew's Hospital were married women, but the rule that Sisters and nurses should be single women or widows was strictly enforced. As a result many of the Hospital staff had no-one to look after them in old age, and continued working until infirmity finally compelled them to give up. One Sister in the 1720s was still working at the age of eighty, but was retired on a pension because her incapacity had led her to set fire to the bed curtains. Others were inclined to disorderly behaviour or drunkenness, and from time to time a nurse was brought before the Governors and reprimanded or dismissed. In 1791 the Governors discharged the entire staff of Luke Ward (Sister, day nurse and night nurse) for being drunk. But offenders on this scale were probably not typical; a more

serious problem was that most nurses had little education and lacked any kind of skill. In the nineteenth century James Paget, the distinguished surgeon, recalled the nurses he had known as a medical student in the 1830s. 'The greater part of them,' he wrote, 'were rough, dull, unobservant and untaught'. The Sisters were generally of higher calibre but, when speaking of the best of the nurses, Paget felt that 'it could only be said that they were kindly, and careful and attentive in doing what they were told'.

The beginnings of professional nursing and nurse education came in the second half of the nineteenth century. In 1868 the Hospital appointed 'scrubbers', and for the first time nurses were relieved of some of their cleaning duties. Then in 1877, following the example of the Nightingale School at St Thomas' Hospital, a School of Nursing was founded at Bart's. In the early years tuition was rudimentary. The older Sisters and staff nurses could offer very little, and as a result the education of the nurses was left to the medical staff. One of the first probationers later wrote her reminiscences of the School in 1877, and recalled the assistance given by the Assistant

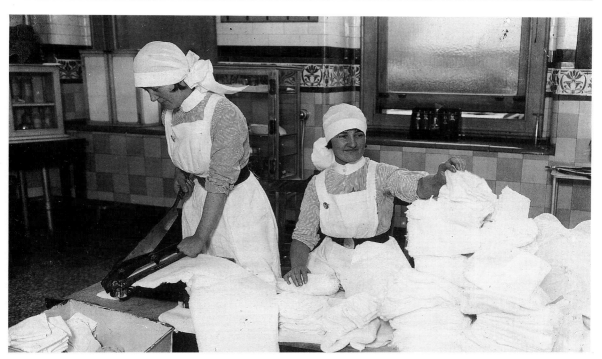

Preparing dressings in the Out-patients Building, c.1929.

Four nurses with a Christmas tree in the Square, c.1930.

Nurses leaving their dining room, c.1934. The nurses' dining room at that time was in the former Casualty Block (now called Lucas Block).

A Sister working at her desk, c.1940.

Surgeon, Alfred Willett, and the Assistant Physician, Dyce Duckworth. Willett 'used to [summon] his out-patient children and teach us to bandage, to put on splints, and so on. Sir Dyce would take us into the wards and give us a lesson on bed-making, poultice-making, or on the contents of the doctor's cupboard...'. One of the medical students showed her how to take a temperature, although this was not then considered a suitable task for a nurse, and she recalled that 'there was generally a row' if a Sister caught one of the probationers using a thermometer.

Initially of one year's duration, the training was soon extended to two years and then, in 1882, to three years. The latter change was made by Ethel Gordon Manson, Matron 1881–7, who was later to marry Dr Bedford Fenwick and to become famous for her devotion to the cause of professional nursing. She was the acknowledged leader of the campaign for state registration of nurses, which was finally granted by Parliament in 1919. In Ethel Manson and her successor, Isla Stewart, Bart's had two of the best-known figures in the progressive nursing movement of that time. Under their leadership working conditions at the Hospital were improved, untrained Sisters and nurses were weeded out, and a full teaching curriculum introduced. By 1910, the

year of Isla Stewart's death, a remarkable transformation had taken place. The nursing establishment of the Hospital had doubled in size, to over 250; and the hours of duty had been reduced from fifteen per day in 1877 to an average of nine. Bart's had by then acquired a world-wide reputation for the quality of its nursing, the excellence of its training school, and the professional commitment of its staff.

Until the 1920s pupils at the School of Nursing were taught by the medical staff, the Matron, or sometimes by one of the ward Sisters. The first Sister Tutor was appointed in 1925, and thereafter a full teaching staff was gradually built up within the School. Lectures continued to be given in the evenings until 1950 when for the first time student nurses were given one full day per week when they could study in the classroom. Shortly afterwards a block system was introduced whereby a month could be spent in the School, away from routine duties in the wards. In 1968 a degree course for student nurses was begun in association with the City University.

The first male nurses arrived in the Hospital in the 1960s and at the same time, with many more student nurses from overseas passing through the School of Nursing, the ethnic composition of the

Sister Tutor lecturing to student nurses, 1961.

nursing staff began to change. Until the 1960s staff nurses' and Sisters' posts were exclusively filled by graduates of the Hospital's own training school, but recruitment practices also changed and by the end of the decade many positions were held by nursing staff who had trained elsewhere. After the report of the Ministry of Health Committee on Senior Nursing Staff Structure (the 'Salmon Report' of 1966) St Bartholomew's, like other hospitals, endeavoured to introduce improved career structures for nurses, and as part of this process the old-established post of Matron was abolished in 1969.

In the mid 1970s the School of Nursing absorbed the former Hackney and Kingsland training schools, the Kingsland school being itself an amalgamation of the teaching facilities at the Metropolitan and St Leonard's Hospitals. The School of Nurs-

ing was renamed in 1989 when it became the St Bartholomew's College of Nursing and Midwifery. By then it had a student body of over 500. Its preregistration course had acquired a strong community emphasis, and students spent time in health centres and home visiting as well as working in hospital. Student nurses had traditionally been employed as part of the Hospital's workforce, but in 1990 the College began a new education programme as part of Project 2000, a national initiative to give student nurses comparable status to polytechnic and university students. An 18-month foundation course, followed by 18 months' specialisation in adult, children's or mental health nursing, was designed to lead to a City University Diploma in Nursing Studies.

THE WARDS

Patients at Bart's have been accommodated in wards since the earliest days of the Hospital's existence. The first record of a ward name dates from 1216, when Alexander de Norfolk granted his house to St Bartholomew's Hospital, specifying that the revenue from it should be used to provide covers for the poor who used the Great Ward as a night shelter. At that time there may well have been only one ward to house all the patients in the Hospital. By 1546 there were three: in May of that year the wards were recorded as 'the inner room called the men's room', with 13 beds, 'the inner room called the women's room', with 22 beds, and 'the outer room where poor men do resort', with 10 beds. Although

there were only 45 beds in total, the sexes were strictly segregated into male and female wards.

After the re-foundation by King Henry VIII the number of wards was increased, and by 1571 there were at least eight. Some of their names – Chapel Ward, Cloister Dorter Ward, Garden Dorter Ward – indicate that old buildings no longer required for monastic purposes had been put to a new use after the Reformation. Inventories from the 1590s in the Hospital archives show that there were then about twelve or thirteen wards, each supervised by a ward Sister.

The names of some of the wards in the late sixteenth and seventeenth centuries – Cutting Ward,

Rahere Ward, West Wing, 1844.

Darker Ward, East Wing, 1899.

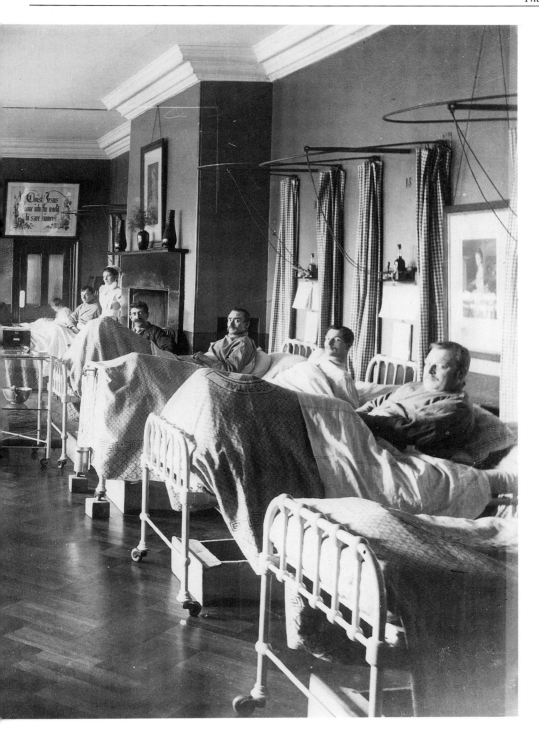

The Prince of Wales visiting a ward at St Bartholomew's Hospital, 1868.

Diet Ward, Sweat Ward – indicate that they were used for a special purpose. Other names – Magdalen, Mary, Martha – were taken from the Bible. New names were introduced in the eighteenth century for the wards in the newly-constructed South, West and East Wings. Some were named after eminent benefactors: Radcliffe Ward, dating from 1740, and Colston Ward, dating from 1752, both commemorate generous gifts to St Bartholomew's. Other wards were named after Presidents and Treasurers of the Hospital. Some of these names – Darker, Marshall, Baldwyn, Powell – are now forgotten, but others such as Harley and Pitcairn survived into recent times.

The South, West and East Wings were designed by James Gibbs with four small wards on each floor, two facing onto the Square and two at the rear. In Gibbs's plan each ward was to have fourteen beds. In the early nineteenth century larger wards were created by demolishing part of the wall that separated each pair of adjoining wards. The enlarged wards were known as 'double' wards, and each had a 'front' part overlooking the Square and a 'back' part behind. It was soon discovered that the 'double' wards could be run more efficiently than the 'single' ones, and by the 1860s all the wards in the Gibbs buildings had been doubled. The practice of

having different wards for medical and surgical patients was well established by the nineteenth century, and when necessary separate accommodation was provided for those with infectious diseases such as cholera.

The earliest surviving pictures of wards in the Hospital date from the first half of the nineteenth century. They show the wooden bedsteads which were still in use in some of the wards at that time. Each was furnished with a flock mattress and bolster, as well as sheets and blankets. Bed curtains had been introduced into the wards as early as 1597; nineteenth century illustrations show semi-circular curtain rails similar to those which remained in use until the 1950s.

In the centre of each ward was an open fireplace, which in nineteenth century winters provided the only source of warmth. Water was pumped to each floor of the building and slipper baths were provided in the wards. Candles were used for lighting until the introduction of gas in the 1840s. There were tables and benches in the wards, but in general the furnishing was very sparse; decorations were unknown and bare wooden floorboards were the rule.

Later illustrations offer a more cheerful picture. By the 1890s there were flower vases and potted

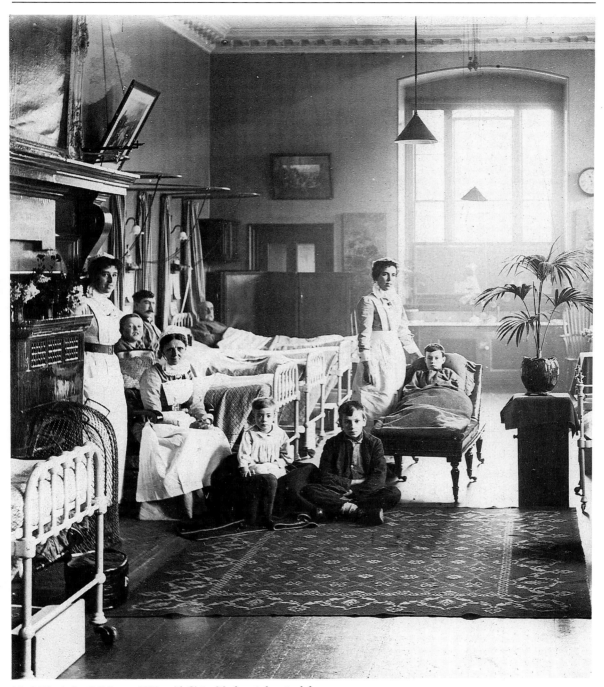

Mark Ward, South Wing, c.1900, with Sister Mark seated centre left.

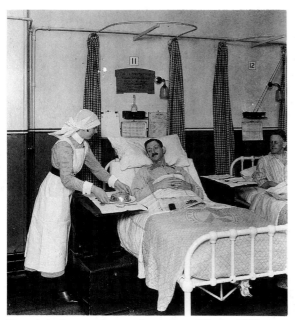

Nurse bringing a meal to a patient in Lucas Ward, c.1929.
Probably posed as a publicity photograph, since Lucas was
actually a female ward at that time.

plants, rugs on the floors and pictures on the walls. Whereas in the earlier part of the century only a few religious books were provided for the patients, by the end of Queen Victoria's reign books and magazines of all kinds were commonplace. The wooden bedsteads had been replaced with iron; on every bed was a counterpane with the Hospital arms. Above the bed hung the patient's notes and prescriptions (and also, from about 1869, a temperature chart); a small wooden shelf was provided for medicines. The check curtains which can be seen in the earliest photographs long remained characteristic of Bart's, and were used in the new wards which opened in the King George V Block in the 1930s.

In the twentieth century the number of wards functioning in the Hospital has fluctuated from time to time, but has generally been about thirty. In the earlier part of the century each firm had an exclusive claim to one male and one female ward, but pressure on space later made it increasingly difficult for whole wards to be assigned in this way. By the beginning of the 1990s it was not unusual for the beds in a ward to be divided between four or five departments.

With a few exceptions, single-sex wards remained the general rule until the opening of the Queen Elizabeth II Wing in 1961; and there were no mixed

Outside Smithfield Ward, West Wing, c.1929.

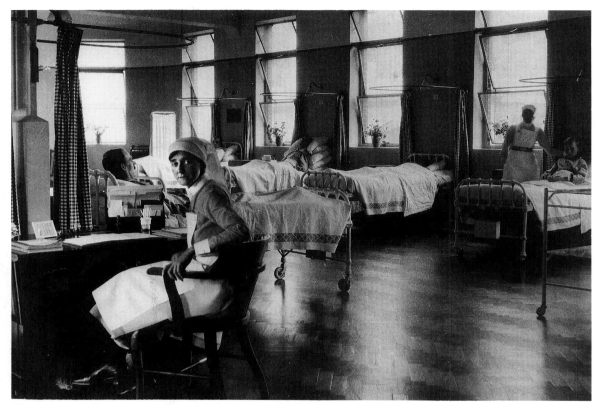

(Above): *Percival Pott Ward, King George V Surgical Block, c.1934.*

(Right): *Nurse pushing a drug trolley in a ward in the King George V Block, 1939.*

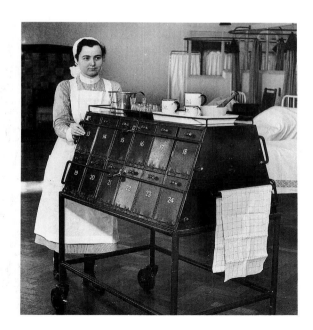

wards in the King George V Block until the 1980s. The Queen Elizabeth II wards also offered smaller rooms, in contrast to the dormitory style of the older wards. More recently this practice has been applied elsewhere as the older blocks have been renovated.

In the early years of the twentieth century the wards were quiet, calm and dignified. The ward Sister ruled with an iron hand over her domain and her small staff of nurses; and the ward routine was centred around the great moment of the day, the Physician's or Surgeon's ward round in the early afternoon, when the great man would proceed from bed to bed followed by his retinue of medical students. Ward rounds are still a regular and important feature of Hospital life, but the consultant no longer expects all other activity to cease on his or her arrival. The wards today are much busier, and their staff much larger, than a century ago; the picture they present to the daytime visitor can often be one of constant activity.

Preparing wartime blackout in the Children's Ward, East Wing, 1939.

PATIENTS

More than eight and a half centuries have passed since the first patients were admitted to St Bartholomew's Hospital. Little information survives about patients in the early days, but a few stories can be found in the manuscript in the British Library which records the life of Rahere. The first patient whose name we know was a man called Adwyne or Alfunyne. He was a carpenter in the once flourishing town of Dunwich in Suffolk, which since his time has all but disappeared under the sea, its streets and houses now destroyed by the erosion of the coastline. He became a patient soon after the foundation of the Hospital in 1123 – certainly within the first twenty years of its existence while Rahere the founder was still alive. We are told that Adwyne had a 'grievous sickness'. He could 'use the free office neither of hand nor of foot; his legs were cleaving to the hinder part of his thighs that he might not go, and his hands turned backwards; nothing with them might he do'. His fingers were 'so rigorously contracted in the sinews' that he could not feed himself. Hearing of the miraculous cures which were said to be taking place there, he travelled by ship to London, where he was brought to Smithfield 'and put in the hospital of poor men'. By the intervention of Saint Bartholomew his condition improved 'and the desired health by certain increments began to come again'. In due course he was able to resume his trade and found employment as a carpenter in the City of London.

From its earliest days Bart's has treated a wide variety of patients. When Pope Lucius III granted the Hospital a papal bull in the early 1180s, he noted that at St Bartholomew's 'a great multitude of the infirm, the poor and the orphaned' received sustenance. In fact the medieval Hospital not only cared for the sick, but also accepted homeless children, pregnant women and the elderly, as well as babies born in the nearby Newgate prison. Wat Tyler is said to have been brought into the Hospital after he was mortally wounded when the ill-fated Peasants' Revolt was crushed at Smithfield in June 1381. However, it is doubtful whether in those early days much could be offered by way of medical treatment; hospitals at that time were religious foundations

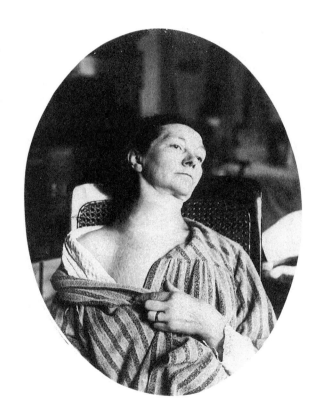

A patient admitted to Sitwell Ward in 1887.

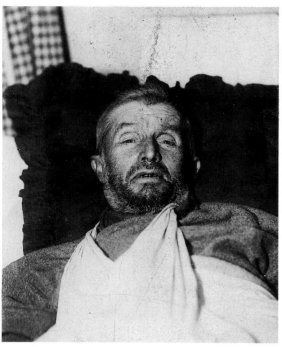

A male patient, 1897.

admitted only on one nominated day each week, exceptions to this rule being made only in emergency cases. Applicants for admission were assembled on the ground floor of the North Wing, where the medical staff selected those who could be admitted to the wards. A further check on admissions was achieved by the Hospital's insistence that, apart from casualty or accident cases, only those with a letter of recommendation from one of the Governors might be admitted. A system of this kind was generally employed in London hospitals in the eighteenth century. However, it meant that many deserving applicants had to be turned away, and it did little for the advancement of medical knowledge within the Hospital since it could deprive the doctors of access to cases of particular interest. In the 1830s the system was modified so that any applicant might be considered for admission, although persons with a Governor's letter might still be preferred. By the end of the nineteenth century Governor's letters had been abandoned.

Although Bart's is deeply rooted in the City of London and many of its patients come from the local communities in London's East End, it has always received patients from far and wide. Adwyne, the first recorded patient, lived on the Suffolk coast and the Hospital's Order Book of 1552 indicates that in the sixteenth century patients were expected from as far away as Northamptonshire. In Victorian times Robert Bridges recalled a woman patient who had travelled to the Casualty Department from Devon, a distance of almost 200 miles, because she had been ill for four months and the local doctors had been unable to cure her sore mouth. In the twentieth century many thousands of patients have been referred to Bart's from all parts of the country and the Hospital's reputation has attracted considerable numbers from overseas.

The range of illnesses treated in the Hospital has changed greatly over the years as advances in medical knowledge have brought about the control of diseases which were once common. In the 1550s there were still cases of leprosy, although these were generally passed on to an 'out-house' such as that at Kingsland, in Hackney, or the Lock, in Southwark. Smallpox, which is now eradicated, was a major threat to health in the eighteenth century, and in 1752 Mark and Luke Wards in the South Wing were set aside for smallpox patients. In the nineteenth century many patients were admitted with typhus or scarlet fever, before the establishment of isolation hospitals. In the twentieth century new treatments for cancer and heart disease have brought large numbers of patients to Bart's. The Hospital now provides highly specialised treatments in many areas while continuing to offer a full range of general acute services.

whose principal object was to provide a comfortable environment for their patients in the hope that rest, regular meals and constant prayer would supply a cure for those who were sick.

After the re-foundation by King Henry VIII in 1546–7, the range of services offered by the Hospital was drastically reduced. The king's charter stated that it was to be a 'house for the relief and sustentation of poor people'. This was interpreted to mean that it could no longer act as an orphanage or as a hospice for the elderly, but was to be exclusively for the benefit of the sick poor. Surgeons, and later physicians, were appointed to provide them with treatment. Between 1547 and 1552 eight hundred patients were discharged as 'cured', while a further 172 had died. The number of beds grew from 45 in 1546 to 100 after the re-foundation, and to more than 200 in the seventeenth century. When the Hospital was rebuilt between 1730 and 1768 it was planned to increase bed numbers to 504, though in the event it was to be some years before this figure was achieved. By 1854 the Hospital had 222 medical and 401 surgical beds, making a total of 623.

Despite the limiting of admissions to the acute sick and the substantial increase in bed numbers, the Hospital could rarely accommodate all the patients who might have claimed its services. Until the middle of the nineteenth century patients were

RULES
TO BE OBSERVED BY THE
PATIENTS
OF
ST. BARTHOLOMEW'S HOSPITAL.

ORDERED,

THAT the Patients shall be obedient to the Regulations respecting the Admission of Visitors, and that Visitors are on no account to drink Tea, Wine, Beer, or other Liquor in the Ward, or remain there longer than the time allowed by the Governors.

THAT no Patient go out of the Hospital without permission from the Physician or Surgeon under whose care such Patient may be placed, nor without the knowledge of the Steward or the Matron. Any Patient having obtained Leave of Absence must return on the same day, before the Gates of the Hospital are closed.

THAT no other Provisions, or Liquors of any kind, be brought into the Wards, than those which have been regularly ordered and supplied for the Use of the Patients.

THAT every Patient who may be able, shall attend the Divine Service on the Sunday Morning, at the Church of St. Bartholomew the Less, if not contrary to their religious principles.

THAT no Patient play at Cards, Dice, or Gamble, or Quarrel, or Blaspheme, or Smoke Tobacco in the Wards.

THAT every Patient must strictly obey the Directions of the Physician or Surgeon under whose care he or she may be placed.

THAT no Reward, in any shape, be given, by a Patient, or his or her Friends, to any Beadle, Sister, Nurse, or other Servant of the Hospital.

THAT any Patient acting contrary to the foregoing Rules will be reported by the Sister of the Ward to the Steward or Matron, and by them to the Treasurer:—such Patient will then be admonished or discharged.

Rules for patients, late nineteenth century.

Arriving by ambulance, c.1929.

Electrocardiograph patient with technician, c.1929.

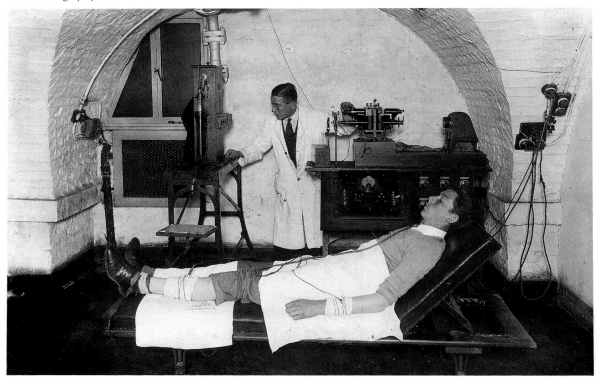

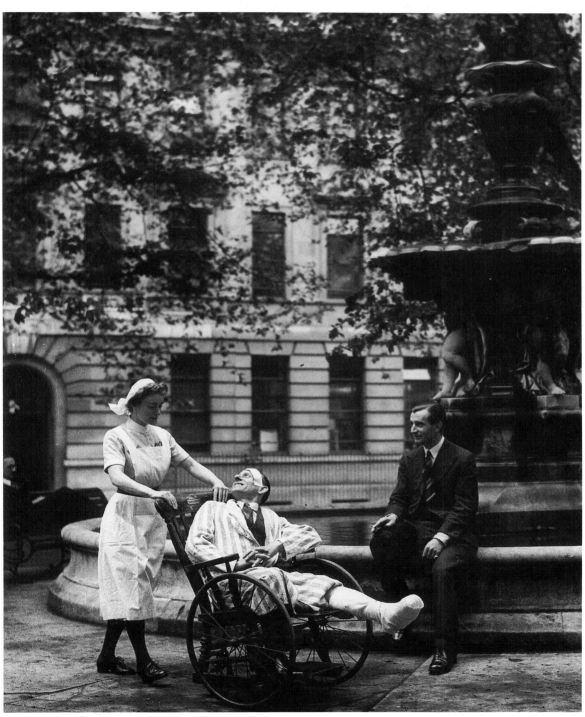

Convalescence in the Square, c.1950.

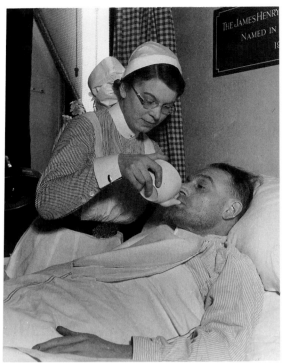

Feeding a post-operative patient, 1940.

One facet of the Hospital's service to patients remained unaltered until fairly recent times. King Henry's charter indicated that St Bartholomew's existed for the benefit of 'poor people', and this remained its stated object until the introduction of the National Health Service. Indeed the word 'patient' is not found in the Hospital's records before the mid seventeenth century. Until that time the men and women treated at Bart's were invariably referred to as 'the poor', and for many years this term remained in use alongside the newer one. 'Prosperity to St Bartholomew's Hospital', ran the traditional toast at Hospital dinners, 'and Health and Ease to the Poor Patients'. In the nineteenth century the majority of adult patients were labourers or domestic servants; many others were unemployed and a considerable number of those who applied for admission were found to be penniless and destitute. It was universally assumed that anyone who was not poor would seek medical treatment at home, and only the impoverished would come to a hospital for relief.

Until the twentieth century Bart's was able to meet its running costs from benefactions and endowment income. As a result, patient treatment was always provided free of charge, apart from gratuities on admission, and even these were abolished in 1821. Once admitted, patients probably found a more comfortable environment, and almost certainly enjoyed better and more regular meals, than they ever had at home. However, they were constantly reminded of the gratitude that was expected of them in return for the Hospital's charity. In the sixteenth century every discharged patient was required to learn by heart and recite aloud a long prayer of thanksgiving for his recovery; and in the nineteenth century strict rules for the patients' behaviour were posted up in all the wards and were read aloud by the ward Sister once a week, with a threat of dismissal from the Hospital for any patient who failed to conform.

In the course of the twentieth century all these attitudes have changed. As the standard of hospital treatment began to improve far beyond anything that could be offered to patients at home it became more difficult to maintain that admission to Bart's was only for 'the poor'; and the establishment of the National Health Service in 1948 meant that the doors of the Hospital could be opened to all, regardless of status. At Bart's, as in other hospitals, the concept of the patient as a recipient of charity has been abandoned and access to medical treatment has become a legal right available to everyone.

MOTHERS AND CHILDREN

Sick children have always been welcomed at Bart's. In the middle ages the numbers of children in the Hospital were sufficient to justify a school within the precincts. There are many moving details recorded in the Hospital's early ledgers and minute books, such as the seven shillings and fourpence paid in 1556 to Goodwife Hall 'for healing of children's heads', or the apprenticeship in 1649 of John Bench, a poor boy who had been left in the Cloisters as an infant of two years old. In the nineteenth and early twentieth centuries Bart's admitted countless children suffering from the various forms of tuberculosis; pneumonia, acute rheumatism, rickets and scurvy were also common.

A Children's Out-patient Department was started in 1904, with Archibald Garrod as the first Physician-in-charge. However, children and adult patients were housed together in the wards until 1930 when the first ward for children was opened in the East Wing. It was known simply as the Children's Ward, having no other name.

Kenton Ward became a children's ward in 1950 when it was reopened after wartime closure. In 1954 Lucas Ward was reopened as a children's ward, and in the same year Kenton Ward moved from the East Wing into Lucas Block. Both of these wards were

A young patient, 1941.

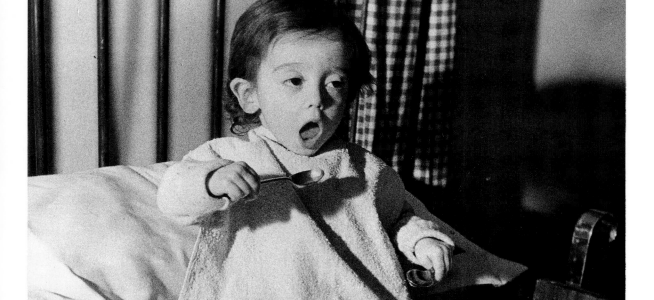

Sister and three nurses bathing new-born babies, c.1930.

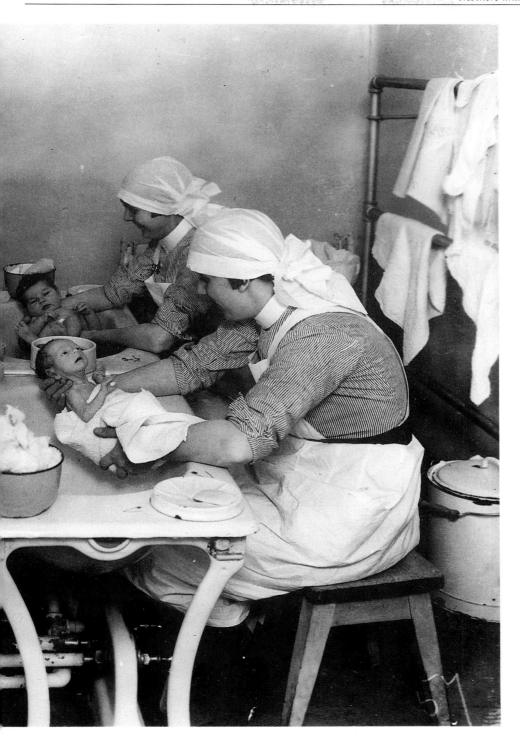

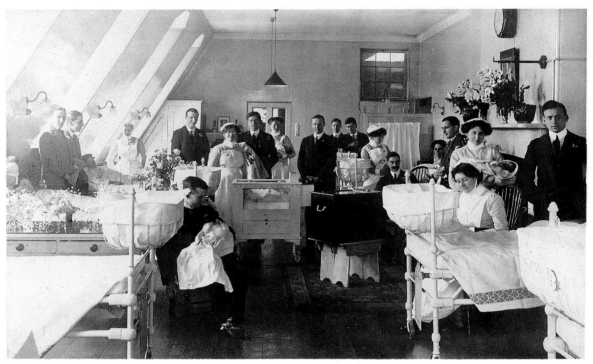

Elizabeth Ward newly equipped as a maternity ward, c.1912.

Children in a spinal carriage, c.1929. This photograph was taken outside a lean-to building (now demolished) adjoining the North Wing.

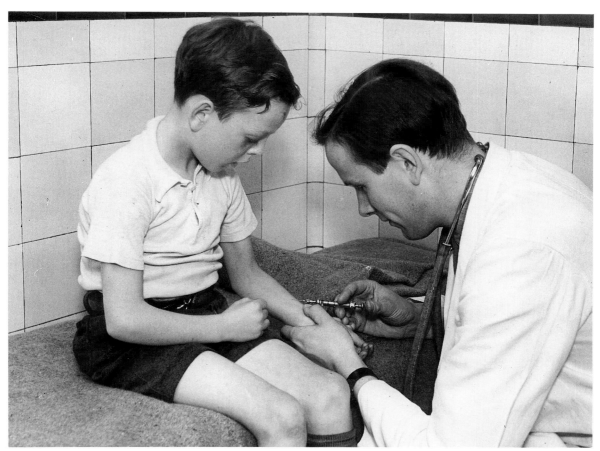

A child being tested for tuberculosis, 1939.

extensively refurbished in 1989–90 and a new Children's Out-patient Unit was constructed in the Lucas Block basement.

For much of its history Bart's had no maternity beds. In the fifteenth century the Hospital accepted women 'that have mysse done that ben whythe chylde', but after the introduction of the Elizabethan poor law the Governors refused to accept maternity cases, apparently fearing that babies born in the Hospital might later become a charge on the parish of St Bartholomew the Less. Despite pressure from the medical staff, who saw the need for students to receive proper teaching in obstetrics, the Governors long maintained their traditional attitude. Not until 1910, in the last days of the poor law, was a lying-in ward established in Elizabeth Ward in the South Wing. Thereafter maternity beds were provided on the Smithfield site until 1986 when the in-patient Obstetric Department was relocated at Homerton.

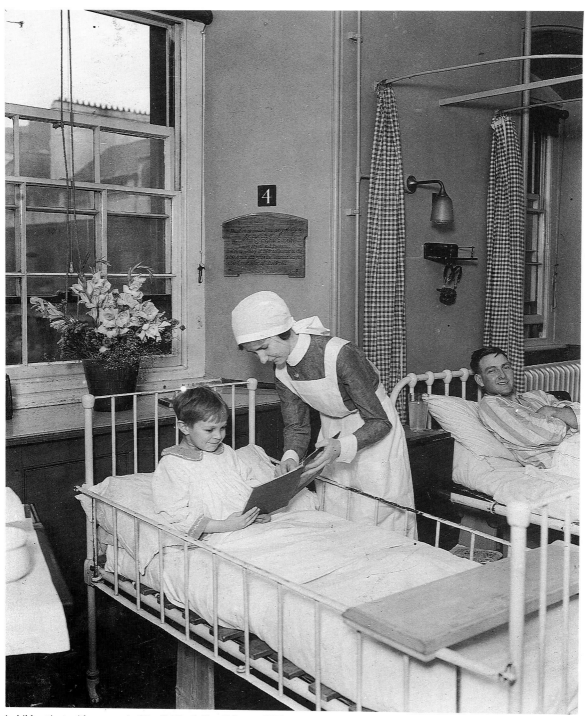

A child patient with a nurse in Sitwell Ward, East Wing, c.1929.

VISITING HOURS

Countless visitors have come to the Hospital over the centuries, and friends and relatives have always been allowed, and sometimes encouraged, to visit patients in the wards. Regulations for visitors seem to have been first introduced in 1767, when the Governors ruled 'that no person shall be permitted to visit any patient before 9 o'clock in the morning, nor after 7 in the evening...[nor] be permitted to remain with any patient longer than one hour in any one day without leave of the Steward or Matron'.

A scarlet fever epidemic in 1887 led to the imposition of severe restrictions and visitors were allowed into the wards only between 2 and 3 o'clock on Sunday afternoons. In 1888 Wednesday afternoon visiting was also permitted, and for many years thereafter the two 'visiting days' were Wednesdays and Sundays. On each of these days a large crowd of visitors would assemble in Smithfield, awaiting the appointed hour when the Henry VIII Gate would be opened to admit them.

An order of the Governors in 1894 introduced admission cards for visitors. Patients who were seriously ill could be visited at any time without a card, but other visitors were expected to obtain one on visiting days. This system continued until the Second World War.

In 1949 the Governors gave their formal agreement to the practice which already existed on many wards, of allowing evening visiting. By the 1960s all wards were opened to visitors on five evenings a week, in addition to Wednesday and Sunday afternoons; and in the children's wards visitors were admitted at any time, at the discretion of the medical and nursing staff.

More recently a policy of open visiting has been introduced throughout the Hospital and on most wards visitors are welcomed at any time after discussion with the ward Sister or Charge Nurse.

St. Bartholomew's Hospital.
GERALDINE MARY HARMSWORTH WARD
Patient's Name _Mrs A. Smith_ No. of Bed } 7

ADMIT ONE VISITOR.

Children under the age of 14 years will not be admitted as Visitors.

This Card must be produced on entering the Hospital Gates, and, when required, in the Wards also. It must be returned to the Sister of the Ward when Patient leaves the Hospital.

VISITING DAYS are—
SUNDAYS .... From 2 to 3.30 o'clock
WEDNESDAYS .... ,, 3 ,, 4 ,,
See Note on back.

Visitor's admission card, c.1932–4.

A visitor sits with a boy patient, c.1929.

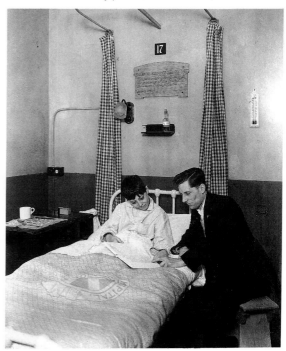

Visitors waiting outside the Henry VIII Gate, 1939.

PORTERS AND BEADLES

The offices of Porter and Beadle are two of the most ancient in the Hospital. In the fifteenth century St Bartholomew's employed a *janitor hospitalis* or doorkeeper, who lived in a house by the Hospital gate; and in 1552 the Porter was instructed that his duty was to guard the doors of the Hospital, 'opening and shutting them in due time, and to give good heed to all such persons as shall pass to and fro'. In the 1550s there were eight Beadles, and their task was to walk the streets of the City, keeping a watch for any sick or diseased persons who should be considered for admission to the Hospital. At the same time the Beadles were to 'have a special eye and regard unto all such persons as have been cured and healed' in the Hospital, 'that none of them counterfeit any grief or disease, neither beg within the City'; they were to report any offenders to the Board of Governors.

Over the years their duties have changed. By the early nineteenth century the Porter had additional responsibility for the Hospital's water pumps and coal supply, for ensuring that all the lamps were lit at night, and also for admitting accident patients at the Porter's lodge. Under him were four Beadles whose duties were, by that time, confined to the Hospital precinct. The Beadles were expected to keep the Hospital free of 'loiterers, beggars, vagrants and all other idle persons'; to carry supplies to the wards; to sweep and keep clean the administrative offices and the outdoor parts of the Hospital; to assist in the mortuary and act as grave-digger and as night watchman; and to maintain the Hospital's fire engine.

The Porter also had important ceremonial duties,

Porters with food trolleys, c.1929.

(Above): *Wheeling a patient, 1939.*

(Left): *Head Porter with gown and staff of office, leading a procession in Smithfield, 1948.*

for which he wore a black gown and carried a staff of office. When the Governors met, he attended them at a service in the church of St Bartholomew the Less and then escorted them to the Great Hall. On the annual View Day in May, when they inspected the wards of the Hospital, he led them in procession and announced their arrival in each ward in turn. The former of these customs has been discontinued. However, View Day is still held every year with the Lord Mayor of London undertaking the Governors' former role; though in recent times the procession has been led, not by the Head Porter, but by one of the Beadles or portering supervisors.

In the twentieth century the Hospital has employed a portering staff of considerable size, with the former single Porter becoming known as the Head Porter and more recently as the Portering Services Manager. The Portering Department remained responsible for the supervision of the Hospital gates until the latter part of the century when this duty passed to a new Department of Risk Management. There are now two Beadles who work in the mortuary; the other members of the portering staff are chiefly employed in escorting patients and in the movement of goods around the Hospital.

THE OUT-PATIENT DEPARTMENTS

The Hospital now treats far more out-patients than in-patients, but this has not always been the case. In the sixteenth century King Henry VIII's charter allowed for in-patient treatment only, and out-patients are not mentioned. The first known reference to them dates from March 1650, when the Governors ordered that all out-patients 'do first procure a certificate of their poverty, that thereby the Governors may be satisfied that they are capable of [i.e., eligible for] the Hospital's charity'. In 1654 the Governors ruled that no more than eight out-patients should be in receipt of 'physic' from the Apothecary at any one time, but in 1659 this was superseded by a regulation imposing a maximum of twenty in any one month. Despite continuing attempts by the Governors to restrict the treatment of out-patients,

Londoners came to the Hospital in ever-increasing numbers. In 1674 a maximum of fifty out-patients was set; in 1707 this was increased to one hundred, and in 1715 to one hundred and fifty. Nevertheless in 1749 it was reported that the average out-patient attendance was 345 per week, or about 18,000 per year. By 1836 the yearly total of out-patients and casualties had grown to 32,000, and by 1846 to over 50,000. In theory, out-patients other than casualties were required to obtain a certificate signed by a Governor before applying for treatment; but in practice this system could not be enforced and by the end of the nineteenth century it had been abandoned.

In the 1830s the patients were seen in rooms adjoining the Apothecary's shop at the rear of the

The waiting hall in the old 'Surgery', 1899.

Sister Surgery (Isabel Armitage) with Nurse Garnett in the Casualty Department stock room, c.1905.

West Wing. At the beginning of Queen Victoria's reign medical out-patients and medical casualties were the responsibility of the three Assistant Physicians, each of whom attended on two days a week. Surgical out-patients were under the charge of the Surgeons to the Hospital, while surgical casualties were seen daily by the dressers and the house surgeons. However by 1840 the number of patients had increased so greatly that the Apothecary's premises could no longer accommodate them all, and two houses in Smithfield near the Henry VIII Gate had been converted into a temporary reception area. Though it was no longer necessary for all the patients to make their way into the crowded precincts of the Hospital, the accommodation was still too small, and in 1842 new purpose-built reception rooms were constructed. These rooms, known as the 'Surgery', were included in the new building – now called Lucas Block – erected at the eastern end of the Hospital's Smithfield frontage. They were enlarged in 1861 and remained in use until the opening of the present Out-patients Building in 1907.

In 1851 Charles Dickens's journal *Household Words* described the scene in the Surgery:

'The patients enter by the colonnade seen from Smithfield. Passing the outer portal, there are two doors, one for women, and one for men; and these lead to two separate rooms. By eleven o'clock these apartments are filled with people of all ages, from the baby a month old, sickening with measles or hooping-cough, to the old crone of seventy, groaning with old age, which she declares to be "roomatiz, which the doctors can cure"...The crowd of patients becomes thicker and thicker, as...the [doctor] enters the scene, with a handful of tickets differently marked. He commences his first examination of the out-patients – a task that looks enough to occupy the whole day. "What is it?" is the rapid inquiry; and while these words come from his tongue, his rapid practised eye is scanning the face of the patient, and his finger is feeling a pulse. The few first words of the patient tell him all he needs; and in another second he has, if it be a trifling case, selected one of the tickets, with the injunction, "Get that medicine. Take a dose twice a day. Come here again the day after tomorrow." In half a moment more another tongue is out, another face has been scanned, and the ticket and direction given; and "What is it?" assails patient number 3; and so the work goes on more rapidly than this description has been written.'

The great speed with which patients were diagnosed was an inevitable result of the vast increase in the numbers who flocked to the Department in the nineteenth century, without any parallel increase in staff at that time. By 1877 when Robert Bridges, later the Poet Laureate, was Casualty Physician at Bart's, annual attendances had grown to almost 152,000. Bridges estimated that he saw an average of 148 patients in a little over three hours each day, at a rate of about one minute and a quarter per patient. Some of his colleagues could see 100 cases in an hour. Most were given a simple prescription, but those who needed more thorough treatment were sent from the Surgery to the medical or surgical out-patient rooms which still existed behind the West Wing.

Attendances continued to rise, reaching a peak of 352,000 in 1911. Until that year any person coming to the Department would be treated; but thereafter, following the passing of the National Insurance Act, the Hospital insisted that insured persons – other than accident and emergency cases – would only be seen on reference from a general practitioner. Attendances fell to 276,000 in 1913, but rose again after the First World War, with figures well in excess of 400,000 per year during the 1930s.

Out-patient Massage Department, c.1920.

Women's out-patient queue, Giltspur Street entrance, c.1929.

A throat examination, c.1929.

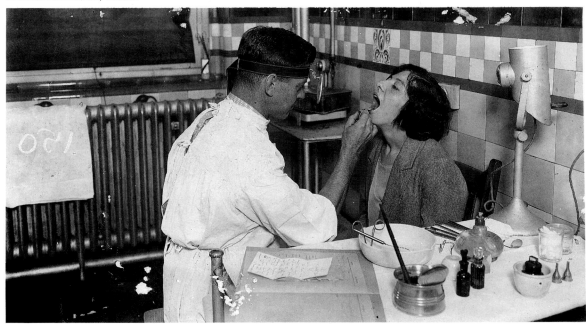

Patients in the waiting hall, c.1929.

Dental Department out-patient clinic, c.1929.

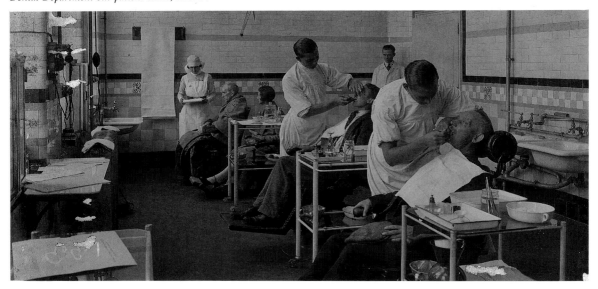

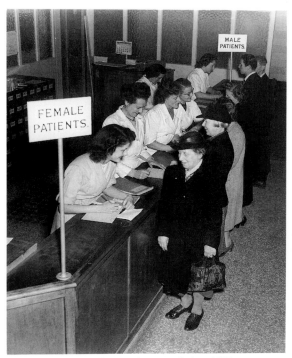

Out-patients and staff at appointments desk, c.1950.

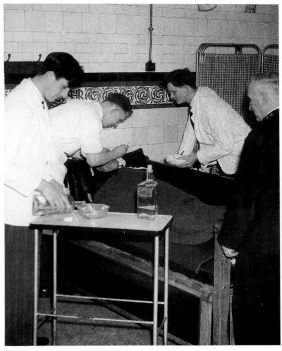

A casualty patient receiving treatment, c.1950.

Since the summer of 1907 the Out-patients and Casualty Departments have been housed in Giltspur Street. By the beginning of the twentieth century there were numerous specialist out-patient clinics, and in the Giltspur Street building each had its own quarters. In 1907 surgical out-patients were seen every day in the morning, and medical out-patients in the afternoon. These Departments were housed on the first floor, where they still remain. Ophthalmic, aural and gynaecological out-patients were seen on the second floor, and dental, dermatological, electrical and orthopaedic on the third. The main waiting hall, which is still in use, was then presided over by Isabel Armitage, Sister Surgery, who had organised much of the transfer from the old building, and who was noted for her even temper and her insistence that the patients seated on the benches should wait in silence.

After the introduction of the National Health Service, casualty attendances, though still large, fell considerably below the levels of the 1930s. By 1964 some of the space in the Casualty Department was under-utilised, and this allowed the Department to be re-designed to accommodate the changing demands on the service. A purpose-built ambulance entrance was constructed at the same time in Windmill Court. This area was again redeveloped in 1988 as the Gateway Resuscitation Unit. The admission of in-patients, formerly dealt with in the Steward's office in the North Wing, is now managed in the main waiting hall. The Giltspur Street building has thus become the main entrance to the Hospital for all patients. In the .waiting hall the benches have gone, and silence is no longer expected. The entrance area now offers refreshments, comfortable chairs and shops selling a wide range of goods.

THE MEDICAL COLLEGE

No single year can be identified as the foundation date of the Medical College, for it grew up imperceptibly within the Hospital over a long period of time. Its corporate seal was first used in 1921, the year when the College and the Hospital were formally separated. The seal bears two other dates: 1123, to commemorate the founding of the Hospital by Rahere, and 1662, to mark the first year in which there is a record of medical students working within the Hospital precinct. On 29 April 1662 the Governors of the Hospital gave orders that 'young gentlemen or doctors or practitioners' should seek permission if they wished to be in attendance when the Hospital's Physicians were prescribing. The Surgeons also had pupils, for two years later the Governors had cause to complain that 'the admittance of patients in the Cloisters was obstructed by the young men that are apprentices to the three Chirurgions, by their pressing importunities [and] bold and saucy carriage'.

The first students doubtless received most of their education by attending in the wards and following the Physicians and Surgeons at their work, a practice which later became known as 'walking the wards' of the Hospital; but by the 1720s Edward Nourse, Assistant Surgeon to St Bartholomew's, was offering lectures to his pupils at his house in Aldersgate Street. In 1734 the Governors for the first time gave consent for any of the Surgeons or Assistant Surgeons 'to read lectures in anatomy in the dissecting-room of the Hospital'. A year later they changed their minds and the permission was withdrawn; but in 1767 the Physicians and Surgeons again approached the Governors, who agreed to allow the reading of lectures in a room adjoining the operating theatre in the newly-built East Wing.

Nevertheless in the 1780s the Hospital staff still found it convenient to give lectures outside the Hospital. In January 1788 advertisements appeared in the name of 'Mr John Abernethy, Assistant Surgeon to St Bartholomew's Hospital', for a course of anatomical lectures to be held at 17 Bartholomew Close, which at that time lay outside the Hospital precinct. However in 1791 the Governors agreed to Abernethy's request for a purpose-built lecture

John Abernethy: a portrait by C.W. Pegler, c.1828.

theatre to be constructed within the Hospital. A theatre was built between Long Row and what was then Windmill Court, behind the West Wing, to the design of George Dance. It was variously known as the 'Surgeons' Theatre', the 'Medical Theatre' and the 'Anatomical Theatre', and lectures were given there by Abernethy (on anatomy, physiology and surgery), John Latham (on medicine), Richard Powell (on chemistry) and others. George Dance's theatre was rebuilt, on the same site but with an enlarged capacity, in 1822. At the same time Abernethy persuaded the Governors to pass a resolution giving formal support to the provision of medical education within the Hospital.

Further accommodation in Long Row was acquired by the Medical School in the course of the nineteenth century. A theatre for chemical lectures was built at the southern end of Long Row, and in 1834–5 a new museum and library were constructed, with a further theatre for lectures on

A certificate of Hospital practice, 1820–1, signed by John Abernethy and two of his colleagues.

The Chemical Lecture Theatre in Long Row, 1849.

materia medica and botany. Thus by the beginning of Queen Victoria's reign all the buildings on the west side of Long Row were employed for medical education. The site has continued to be used in this way, and in recent years has been occupied by the Robin Brook Centre and the Department of Medical Illustration, the latter being housed in the remodelled nineteenth century building which was originally the chemical lecture theatre.

In Abernethy's time, and for some years afterwards, a student decided his own curriculum, attending lectures as he wished, besides walking the wards. If he preferred, he could choose to attend lectures at several different hospitals or private medical schools. At Bart's, as elsewhere, students paid no lecture fees to the Hospital, but could purchase admission tickets to as many individual courses as they wished to attend. Each lecturer sold tickets for his own courses. At the end of a course a certificate of attendance might be granted to those who had completed it. Certificates of 'Hospital practice' were also issued, to students who had attended regularly in the wards.

After Abernethy's death in 1831 the School began to decline, since no member of the medical staff was prepared to take responsibility for administering it,

or for offering guidance to the students in the development of their studies. Until 1843 students had to arrange their own accommodation, but in that year the Governors founded a residential college which, in the words of the old *College Calendars*, was intended 'to afford the pupils the moral advantages, together with the convenience, of a residence within the walls of the Hospital'. The terminology used in the nineteenth century differed from that of the present day; the educational institution was known as the Medical School, while the 'College' referred only to the residential quarters. These occupied a row of houses on the west side of Duke Street (now called Little Britain). The first Warden of the College was the young James Paget, who had already distinguished himself by his discovery of *trichinella spiralis* while he was still a medical student, at the age of 21. As Warden, Paget soon found himself directing the studies not only of the residents, but also of those students who lived outside. Paget's dedication to this task quickly re-established the prestige of the School, and thereafter successive Wardens became in effect the administrators of the School and the keepers of its accounts.

In 1850 Paget was largely responsible for the welcome which Bart's extended to Elizabeth Blackwell

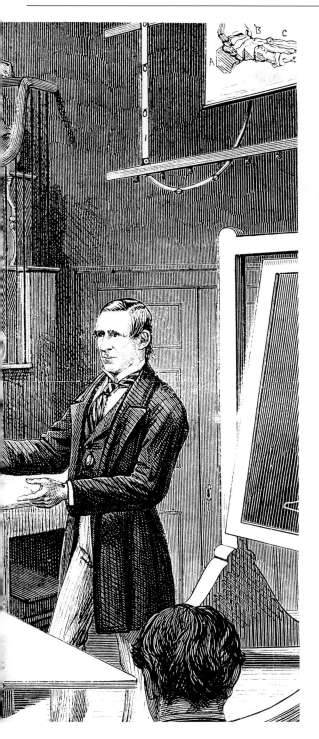

(Left): *James Paget lecturing at St Bartholomew's Hospital, 1874.*

(Top): *B.W. Quartey-Papafio, a medical student in the late nineteenth century.*

(Below): *Lecture admission ticket issued by James Paget, 1857.*

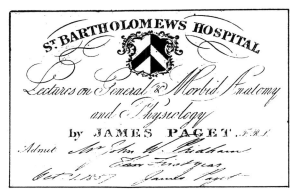

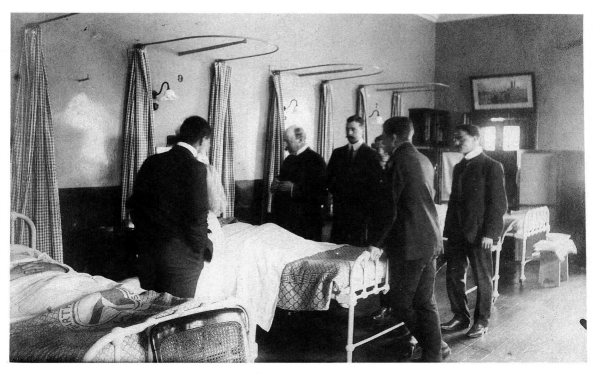

Medical students on a ward round, 1906. The Physician in this photograph is thought to be James Calvert.

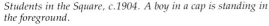

Students in the Square, c.1904. A boy in a cap is standing in the foreground.

an Anglo-American lady who became the first qualified female medical practitioner. From May 1850 until July 1851 she was the first, and only, female student in the Medical School at St Bartholomew's. She walked the wards with the Physicians and Surgeons of the day, attended Paget's lectures on pathology, and was instructed in the Museum by two of the younger surgeons, Luther Holden and Holmes Coote. The novelty of a lady student ensured that she received a kindly welcome from all the staff. In later life she recalled that 'Dr [Clement] Hue was especially friendly…showing me everything of interest in his wards; and my notebooks are full of valuable observations made under his guidance'.

After her departure, however, a more conservative outlook prevailed in the School, and for many years any suggestion that female students should be admitted met with strenuous resistance. Women students continued to be excluded until 1947.

In the early years of the School practically all the students were of British nationality, but from the late nineteenth century onwards increasing numbers from overseas have been admitted. The first black student was probably B.W. Quartey-Papafio from Accra in the Gold Coast, who entered the School in November 1882 and became the first Ghanaian to qualify as a medical practitioner.

Until 1892 the regulations of the Royal College of Physicians and Royal College of Surgeons required four years' study for a professional qualification, of which only thirty months had to be spent at a hospital medical school; but after that date five years' study became the norm. By 1900 the winter session at St Bartholomew's offered lectures, classes and demonstrations in the different branches of medicine, surgery, anatomy and physiology, biology, chemistry, pathology, and bacteriology. The summer session provided tuition in forensic, ophthalmic and psychological medicine, materia medica and pharmacology, midwifery, and public health. The fee for five years of study was 150 guineas, if paid in one sum on entrance, or 160 guineas if paid in four annual instalments.

As early as 1839 the teaching at the Medical School had been recognised by the University of London in admitting candidates for medical degrees. In 1900 the School became one of the constituent colleges of the University, but it remained a voluntary association of teachers in the Hospital with no legal status of its own until after the First World War. A new post of Dean was created in 1904 and the postholder became effectively the head of the School, although the older position of Warden was retained until 1973. In 1919 Medical and Surgical Professorial Units were established, in anticipation of a formal alteration in the status of the School; and in 1921 the School was incorporated by royal charter with a new title, the Medical College of St Bartholomew's Hospital in the City of London.

In 1933–4, while William Girling Ball was Dean, the Medical College purchased the site of the former Merchant Taylors' School in Charterhouse Square. This acquisition enabled it to rehouse the pre-clinical departments, which were previously in cramped quarters on the west side of Giltspur Street. In the Second World War, however, the College suffered badly. Most of the buildings on the Charterhouse Square site were damaged or destroyed; and on the Smithfield site the buildings in Long Row, including the Anatomical and Medical Lecture Theatres, were also wrecked. At the outbreak of war the College had at once introduced temporary teaching arrangements for the period of hostilities. Pre-clinical students were evacuated to Queens' College, Cambridge, while clinical teaching was divided between St Bartholomew's, Hill End Hospital at St Albans, and Friern Hospital,

W.H. Hurtley, Reader in Chemistry, in the chemical laboratory, c.1930.

Students attending a lecture, c.1937–8.

New Southgate. The pre-clinical school returned to London in 1946, but the rebuilding of the Charterhouse Square site took many years and was not completed until 1963. Construction of the Robin Brook Centre for Medical Education in Long Row began in 1979 and the Centre was opened in June 1980.

Student life at Bart's in the post-war years has been immortalised in the humorous books of Richard Gordon; *Doctor in the House* is based on a true episode in 1957 when 'Percy', the College mascot, was purloined by students from Guy's Hospital after an inter-collegiate rugby match. In the 1960s the College acquired its first regular peacetime teaching facilities outside Bart's when seventy general medical beds were made available to it at St Leonard's Hospital. After the establishment of the City and Hackney Health District in 1974 it became possible for all students to receive part of their training at Hackney Hospital, and more recently at Homerton. Other hospitals used for clinical teaching in recent years have included Whipps Cross, North Middlesex and Southend.

Following the recommendations of the Royal Commission on Medical Education in 1968, a close

association with The London Hospital Medical College was developed, and a number of joint academic departments were established. After protracted discussions a controversial scheme for the merger of the two colleges was abandoned, and in 1986 agreement was reached to form a City and East London Confederation within the University of London. A Joint Faculty of Basic Medical Sciences was established at Queen Mary and Westfield College, Mile End, and in 1990 the pre-clinical departments in Charterhouse Square were closed. Students from both Bart's and The London now spend the first two years of their course at Queen Mary and Westfield College. Space released on the Charterhouse Square site has been used to develop clinical and para-clinical units, both as College departments and as associated institutes.

At the beginning of the twentieth century the College was devoted almost exclusively to undergraduate teaching, but in the second half of the century it has also acquired a world-wide reputation for innovative research in many fields of medicine. The St Bartholomew's Clinical Research Centre was opened in 1982 in Dominion House, Bartholomew Close.

Wartime bomb damage to the Medical Lecture Theatre at the north end of Long Row, 1940.

The Pathological Museum

The earliest record of a museum at St Bartholomew's dates from 1726, when the Governors gave orders concerning two rooms which had been prepared, 'one for the more decent laying the dead patients before their burial, the other a repository for anatomical or chirurgical preparations'. These rooms were on the ground floor of the building containing the Cutting Ward, on the west side of the Long Walk (close to where the southern end of the West Wing now stands). The Governors' instructions were 'that whatever preparation shall be given

to the repository shall be numbered, and the name of the person who gave it and the history of it be entered in a book'. The first curator was John Freke, at that time Assistant Surgeon to the Hospital; it was ordered 'that Mr Freke do keep the key...[and] be accountable for the loss of any preparation'.

In the 1820s the Museum was housed in a room adjoining the carpentry shop behind the West Wing, on the site now occupied by the Robin Brook Centre. A new and larger museum was erected in 1834–5 on approximately the same site, and was

The Museum in 1899.

Studying specimens in the Museum, c.1929.

again extended in 1854. The present Museum was constructed in 1878–9 to the design of Edward I'Anson; it remains largely as it was built, a splendid example of the architecture of its time.

No specimens from John Freke's day are now in the Museum, and the book in which their details were entered no longer exists. The oldest surviving specimen is a congenital inguinal hernia dissected by Percival Pott, probably in the early 1750s, shortly after his appointment as Surgeon to the Hospital. The largest numbers of specimens were added to the collection in the late nineteenth and early twentieth century, the heyday of the Museum, when its holdings formed one of the most important teaching resources for students in the Medical School. In Victorian times the Museum included anatomical as well as pathological material, but the anatomical

specimens were subsequently transferred to a separate collection maintained by the Anatomy Department. The latter items were taken to Queen Mary and Westfield College at Mile End when the Anatomy Department moved there in 1990. At the same time one of the historical curiosities in the collection, the skull of John Bellingham, the assassin of Prime Minister Spencer Perceval in 1812, was returned from the Anatomy Department and again placed on display in the Pathological Museum.

The development of new teaching methods in recent years has altered the Museum's role in medical education, but the collection is still used for teaching purposes and the Museum itself remains a regular tutorial venue. It is not usually open to the public.

THE MEDICAL COLLEGE LIBRARY

The Library of St Bartholomew's Hospital Medical College was originally a private library. It was founded in 1800 by members of the Medical and Philosophical Society of St Bartholomew's Hospital (later known as the Abernethian Society), who met to read and discuss papers on medical subjects. The Society later entrusted its book collection to the Board of Governors of the Hospital. The books were housed in a room on the second floor of the East Wing until a new library building was erected in 1834–5. This building was situated at the northern end of Long Row, a little to the south-west of the

present Library. Until about 1880 the Library was maintained by contributions from the medical staff and subscriptions from students and others who wished to use the reading room or borrow books. It became the property of the Medical College on its incorporation in 1921.

The present building was constructed in 1878–9 and was opened in November 1879 by the Prince of Wales, later King Edward VII. The interior was renovated in 1959 and again in 1979. A new branch library on the Charterhouse Square site was opened in 1962, replacing a temporary building there.

The Library building in Long Row, 1844.

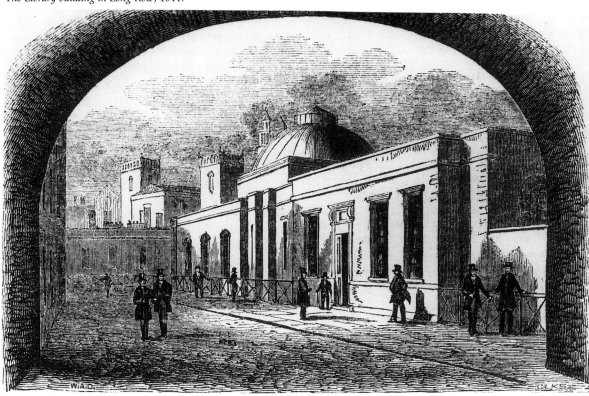

The opening of the new Library, 1879.

Library interior, 1899.

Subscriber's ticket, 1851.

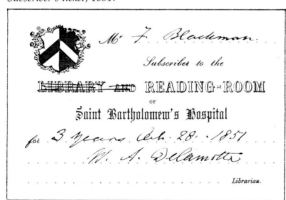

The Library now has a collection of 60,000 volumes, and is open to all staff and students who need access to medical literature. Its holdings include material on medical history and biography, and a substantial collection of older books by authors associated with St Bartholomew's Hospital.

THE ARCHIVES

St Bartholomew's is fortunate in possessing the finest collection of hospital archives in the English-speaking world. The oldest records date from the twelfth century, shortly after the foundation of the Hospital by Rahere, and the collection extends from those early times to the present day.

Throughout the ages the Hospital has shown concern for the security and good management of its written records. The Hospital's Order Book published in 1552 contained 'an order for the safe keeping of the evidences and writings appertaining to the Hospital'; it stated that 'there shall one fair and substantial chest be provided, and the same be set in the most convenient and surest place of the house, which shall have three several locks and three keys...and it shall not be lawful to any of the Governors to have any evidence or writing out of the said chest...but only a copy thereof, which shall be taken in the presence of the three persons that have the keys, and the original forthwith to be locked up again'.

A strong room for the Hospital records was constructed in the basement of the North Wing in 1820. In October 1841 the Clerk to the Governors, William Wix, reported that he had drawn up a schedule of the contents of the boxes in the muniment room, adding that 'many of the deeds and papers being intermixed, the list and index has occupied a considerable time and required much care in the preparation; the title deeds being numerous and many of them from their antiquity very difficult to decipher'. A later Clerk, William Henry Cross, also took an active interest in the archives; he was a competent scholar and in 1883 and the years which followed he began work on sorting and cataloguing the medieval records.

The scale of the task meant that Cross was unable to finish it. In the twentieth century the Clerks, and their successors as Hospital Administrators and General Managers, have had neither the time nor the scholarly inclination to manage the Hospital's historical records. The need for a curator was first recognised in 1934 when D'Arcy Power, a former Surgeon to the Hospital, was appointed Keeper of

Seal of St Bartholomew's Hospital, on a deed of about 1200 in the Hospital Archives.

(Overleaf): *A plan of the Hospital precinct, c.1617.*

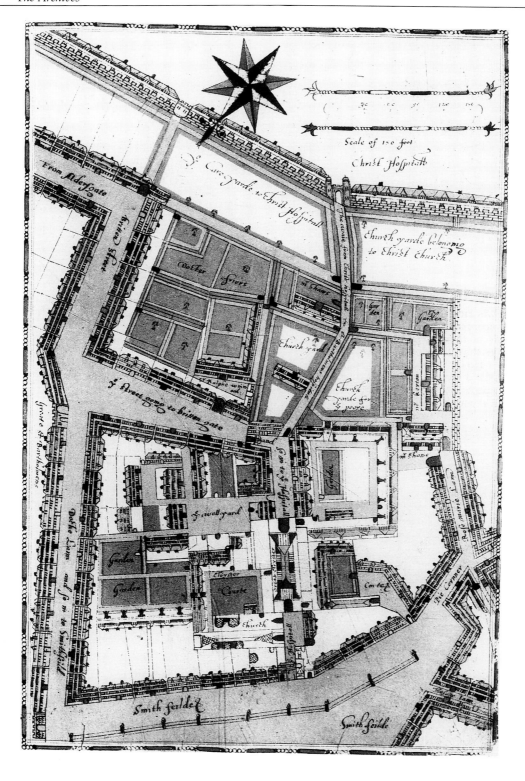

the Muniments. The first professionally qualified Archivist was appointed in 1951, and in 1964 the Archives Department was formally appointed by the Lord Chancellor as a place of deposit for public records under section 4 (1) of the Public Records Act 1958. Temperature- and humidity-controlled strongrooms for the Department were constructed in the Clerk's House in 1965–6.

The Department's holdings include many thousands of title deeds (including almost 2000 dating from before the Reformation); two fifteenth century cartularies; the minute books of the Board of Governors from 1549 to 1974; financial accounts from 1547 to the present day; maps and plans from 1587 onwards; and numerous rentals, surveys and estate papers. Medical records survive from 1826, and there are papers relating to almost every aspect of the Hospital's development in the nineteenth and twentieth centuries. The Department now assists in the preservation of essential modern records, besides caring for those which have been inherited from earlier times; it also provides a service to St Bartholomew's Hospital Medical College.

Modern records are initially selected for retention on the basis of their value for management purposes within the Hospital, and to meet legal requirements. However, gifts of private papers, photographs and other material relevant to the collection are also welcomed. There is no permanent exhibition of the archives, but the older records can be made available, by prior appointment, to those undertaking historical or medical research.

D'Arcy Power, Surgeon, noted medical historian, and first curator of the Archives; photograph taken in the Square on View Day 1938.

FURTHER READING

The publications listed below are all available in the Library of St Bartholomew's Hospital Medical College.

SMITHFIELD
A. Forshaw and T. Bergstrom, *Smithfield Past and Present* (London, 1980)

THE HENRY VIII GATE
G. Whitteridge, 'The Henry VIII Gateway into Smithfield', *St Bartholomew's Hospital Journal* Jul. 1949 pp.148–50

THE CHURCH OF ST BARTHOLOMEW THE LESS
G. Whitteridge, 'The Parish Church of St Bartholomew the Less', *St Bartholomew's Hospital Journal* Dec. 1951 pp.260–4
G. Whitteridge and M.V. Stokes, *A Brief History of the Hospital of St Bartholomew* (London, 1961) pp.65–8
V.C. Medvei and J.L. Thornton (eds.), *The Royal Hospital of St Bartholomew 1123–1973* (London, 1974) pp.36–42

THE SQUARE
D'Arcy Power, 'The Rebuilding of the Hospital in the Eighteenth Century', *St Bartholomew's Hospital Reports* 1926 pp.9–34 and 1927 pp.7–24

THE FOUNTAIN
M.V. Stokes, 'The Centenary of the Fountain', *St Bartholomew's Hospital Journal* Oct. 1959 pp.261–2

THE GREAT HALL AND THE HOGARTH PAINTINGS
N. Moore, *The History of St Bartholomew's Hospital* (London, 1918) vol. 2 pp.847–52
W.M. Eccles, 'The Paintings of Hogarth', *St Bartholomew's Hospital Journal* Feb. 1935 pp.99–101
R. Sanders, 'William Hogarth', *St Bartholomew's Hospital Journal* Apr. 1964 pp.157–61
N.J.M. Kerling, 'Pictures in the Hospital', *St Bartholomew's Hospital Journal* Jul. 1971 pp.212–14
V.C. Medvei and J.L. Thornton (eds.), *The Royal Hospital of St Bartholomew 1123–1973* (London, 1974) pp.288, 294, 332–7

LUCAS BLOCK AND SURGERY HOUSE
G. Yeo, '150th Anniversary of Lucas Block', *Barts Journal* Spring 1992 pp.14–15

BARTHOLOMEW CLOSE
E.A. Webb, *The Records of St Bartholomew's Priory... Smithfield* (Oxford, 1921) vol. 2 pp.181–7, 213–20

QUEEN ELIZABETH II WING
W.A. Guttridge, 'The New Surgical In-Patients Block in Little Britain', *St. Bartholomew's Hospital Journal* Oct. 1957 pp.313–17

KING GEORGE V BLOCK
T.A. Lodge, 'The New Surgical and Operation Blocks', *St Bartholomew's Hospital Reports* 1930 pp.19–28
T.A. Lodge, 'The King George V Building', *St Bartholomew's Hospital Journal* Aug. 1937 pp.208–10

CHARTERHOUSE SQUARE
A.H. Coughtrey, 'A Note on the History of the Charterhouse', *St Bartholomew's Hospital Journal* Nov. 1933 pp.29–31
W. Girling Ball, 'The Beginnings of the New Medical College', *St Bartholomew's Hospital Journal* Nov. 1935 pp.25–31
W. Girling Ball, 'The New Medical College of St Bartholomew's Hospital', *St Bartholomew's Hospital Reports* 1936 pp.41–53
M.V. Stokes, 'Charterhouse – the Medieval Foundation', *St Bartholomew's Hospital Journal* Aug. 1955 pp.261–3

PHYSICIANS AND SURGEONS
N. Moore, *The History of St Bartholomew's Hospital* (London, 1918) vol. 2 pp.421–755
D'Arcy Power, *A Short History of St Bartholomew's Hospital* (2nd ed., London, 1935) pp.44–50, 96–118
V.C. Medvei and J.L. Thornton (eds.), *The Royal Hospital of St Bartholomew 1123–1973* (London, 1974) pp.104–241

OPERATIONS AND OPERATING THEATRES
G.E. Gask, 'Cutting Wards and Operation Theatres', *St Bartholomew's Hospital Journal* Oct. 1934 pp.6–8
J.L. Thornton, 'Development of the Department of Anaesthetics', *St Bartholomew's Hospital Journal* Jan. 1959 pp.13–17
V.C. Medvei and J.L. Thornton (eds.), *The Royal Hospital of St Bartholomew 1123–1973* (London, 1974) pp.216–17, 250

THE ELECTRICAL AND X-RAY DEPARTMENTS
W.E. Steavenson, 'The Electrical Department', *St Bartholomew's Hospital Reports* 1883 pp.235–47
Anon., 'Dr Lewis Jones and the Electrical Department', *St Bartholomew's Hospital Journal* Jun. 1912 pp.162–4

I.G. Williams, 'The Mozelle Sassoon One Million Volt X-ray Therapy Department', *St Bartholomew's Hospital Journal* Jul. 1961 pp.163–5

N.S. Finzi, 'The Early Days of Radiotherapy at Bart's', *St Bartholomew's Hospital Journal* Nov. 1964 pp.468–70

H. Jackson Burrows, 'Pioneer Radiology at Bart's', *Bart's Journal* Autumn 1986 pp.29–31

APOTHECARIES, DISPENSERS AND PHARMACISTS

D'Arcy Power, *A Short History of St Bartholomew's Hospital* (2nd ed., London, 1935) pp.118–23

W.S. Church, 'Our Hospital Pharmacopoeia and Apothecary's Shop', *St Bartholomew's Hospital Reports* 1884 pp.279–308 and 1886 pp.1–54

W.S. Church, 'St Bartholomew's Hospital and Medicine during the last Fifty Years', *St Bartholomew's Hospital Journal* Jul. 1912 pp.173–9

NURSES

S. Paget, *Memoirs and Letters of Sir James Paget* (London, 1902) pp.353–4

N. Moore, *The History of St Bartholomew's Hospital* (London, 1918) vol. 2 pp.756–78

N.J.M. Kerling, 'Nursing in St Bartholomew's Hospital in the Seventeenth Century', *St Bartholomew's Hospital Journal* Aug. 1970 pp.278–80

V.C. Medvei and J.L. Thornton (eds.), *The Royal Hospital of St Bartholomew 1123–1973* (London, 1974) pp.242–61

W.E. Hector, *100 Years in the School of Nursing* (London, 1977)

J. Foster, 'Nurses' Uniforms through the Ages', *The Bart's Journal* Summer 1983 pp.26–8

THE WARDS

G. Yeo, *Ward Names at Bart's* (London, 1990)

PATIENTS

N. Moore, *The History of St Bartholomew's Hospital* (London, 1918) vol. 2 pp.863–86

D'Arcy Power, *A Short History of St Bartholomew's Hospital* (2nd ed., London, 1935) pp.27–35

MOTHERS AND CHILDREN

D'Arcy Power, *A Short History of St Bartholomew's Hospital* (2nd ed., London, 1935) pp.113–15

A. Robinson, 'The Children's Department', *St Bartholomew's Hospital Journal* Apr. 1965 pp.158–62

PORTERS AND BEADLES

D'Arcy Power, *A Short History of St Bartholomew's Hospital* (2nd ed., London, 1935) pp.68–74

THE OUT-PATIENT DEPARTMENTS

R. Bridges, 'An Account of the Casualty Department', *St Bartholomew's Hospital Reports* 1878 pp.167–82

Anon., 'Description of the New Out-patient and Casualty Block', *St Bartholomew's Hospital Journal* Aug. 1907 pp.171–3

Anon., 'Twenty-four Hours in a London Hospital', *St Bartholomew's Hospital Reports* 1924 pp.5–21

J.O. Robinson, 'Alterations in the Casualty Department', *St Bartholomew's Hospital Journal* Jun. 1962 pp.127–8 and Apr. 1964 pp.149–51

THE MEDICAL COLLEGE

E. Blackwell, 'A Reminiscence of Forty Years Ago', *St Bartholomew's Hospital Journal* Sep. 1894 pp.191–2

S. Paget, *Memoirs and Letters of Sir James Paget* (London, 1902) pp.39–183

A. Willett, 'Our Medical School as I first knew it', *St Bartholomew's Hospital Journal* Jan. 1911 pp.51–4

J.L. Thornton, *John Abernethy* (London, 1953) pp.26–34, 61–5

C. Morris, 'The Medical College and its Administration', *St Bartholomew's Hospital Journal* Oct. 1963 pp.297–9

V.C. Medvei and J.L. Thornton (eds.), *The Royal Hospital of St Bartholomew 1123–1973* (London, 1974) pp.43–103

THE PATHOLOGICAL MUSEUM

F.S. Eve, 'Our Museum and its Associations', *St Bartholomew's Hospital Reports* 1881 pp.165–84

T.H.G. Shore, *A Descriptive Catalogue of the Pathological Museum of St Bartholomew's Hospital* (London, 1929)

V.C. Medvei and J.L. Thornton (eds.), *The Royal Hospital of St Bartholomew 1123–1973* (London 1974) pp.354–67

THE MEDICAL COLLEGE LIBRARY

A.H. Coughtrey, 'Our Library', *St Bartholomew's Hospital Journal* Dec. 1934 pp.65–7

V.C. Medvei and J.L. Thornton (eds.), *The Royal Hospital of St Bartholomew 1123–1973* (London, 1974) pp.308–31

THE ARCHIVES

N.J.M. Kerling, 'The Department of Archives', *St Bartholomew's Hospital Journal* Dec. 1964 pp.493–4

V.C. Medvei and J.L. Thornton (eds.), *The Royal Hospital of St Bartholomew 1123–1973* (London, 1974) pp.299–307

G. Yeo, 'The Archives', *Barts Journal* Summer 1988 pp.26–7

THE ILLUSTRATIONS

Illustrations in this book, taken from originals in the Archives of St Bartholomew's Hospital, have the following references:

Index

Entries in bold type
refer to illustrations

SUBSCRIBERS

The publication of this book was made possible by the support of the following individuals who subscribed for advance copies. Many of the subscribers possess academic or other distinctions but these have had to be omitted for reasons of space.

Mrs Mary Abbis (née Rand)
Maeve C. Abbott
Geoffrey Charles Acres and Peter F. Acres
John and Margaret Acton
Miss Lisbeth Adams
Mrs Kristin E.A. Addison
Margaret Aitken
Mrs Diana Aitken-Wiseman
Dr and Mrs M.H. Alawi
Dr David E. Alder
Marjorie Alderton
Mrs V.E. Aldhous
Mrs Shelagh Aldred
Kay Allan
Mrs S.A. Allan (Allan)
Miss E.A.P. Allen
Dr Julian Allen
Sheila M. Allen
Sybil Allen
Eve Allibone
Marion Allison
Mrs C. Allum
Dr David J. Alston
Dr Christopher G. Alveyn and Dr Mary E. Rogerson
Dr T.A.S. Amos
A.R. Anderson
Alan and Rosemary Anderson
Mrs J. Andrew
Miss Jane Andrew
R.H. Andrews
Mr Henry George Annan
Prof. Peter P. Anthony
Susan V. Anthony (née Zambra)
George H. Apthorp
Jenny E.A. Archer
Helen Archer-Lock
Marilyn Armitstead
Jane Armston
John Henry Armstrong
Margaret M. Arnold
Peter Arundell
Fiona Ash and John Wischmeyer
Dr M.A. Ashby
Dr and Mrs P.A. Ashby
Elizabeth Atchison
Edmund C. Atkinson
Heather Atkinson (Williams)
Mrs M.V. Atkinson
Margaret L. Atkinson
Roana W. Atkinson
Judith Aubrey
Dr and Mrs A.J. Austin
J.F. Avery Jones
Jill Axtell (Swannell)
T.M. Ayoub

David Badham
Miss M.E.G. Bagnall
Mr and Mrs Hillary A. Bagshaw
A.G.S. (Joe) Bailey
Alan Bailey
Dr Guy R.M. Baker
Mary Savage Baker
Philippa and David Baker
Jean Balcombe (J.P. Grace)
Ann Susan Baldock
Miss Jacqueline Ballard
Mrs Thelma Ballinger
Elisabeth A. Bamforth (née Fearnside)
A. Allan Bapty
Diana E. Barber
Shelagh Barber
Belinda J. Barclay
R.M. Bark
Gill Barker
Valerie A. Barker (née Lloyd)
Mr and Mrs M.D. Barlow
J. Barnard
Greta Barnes
Dr N.D. Barnes
Barbara Barnett (née Cumber)
Michael Barnham
Dr and Mrs Marshall Barr
R.F. Barrett
Dr Ian and Mrs K.M. Barrow
Sarah C. Bate
A. Daunt Bateman
Mrs Jocelyn Batiste
Keith L. Batten
Carol Bavin
Harold Leslie Whitchurch Beach
Ursula Beasley
Heather Beckwith
Shelagh Bedford-Turner
Mr and Mrs R.C. Bell
Dr and Mrs J.T. Bench
M.E. Benfield
Evelyn Bennett (Morley)
Mrs J.M. Robin Bennett
Julie Bennett
Mary Bennett
Richard Benson
Mrs Enid Susan Berg
W.M. Berry
Dr John Berth-Jones
Prof. Michael Besser
Dr and Mrs D.W. Bethune
Sheelagh Bewley
Mrs Jeanne Beyer (née Maury)
M.A. Bezwoda
J.A.R. Bickford
Mrs Philip Bickford Smith (née Angela Minnekeer)

Mrs N.R. Bigland (E.M. Spreckley)
Dr Tim R.M. Billington
Dr B.J. Bintcliffe
Ian Bintcliffe
Sally Bisby
Sally Bishop
Dr J.R. Blackburne
Mary Tuckwell Blake
P.R. Blakesley
Miss Elizabeth A.P. Bloy
Mrs Jean K. Boddy
Dr and Mrs A.R. Bodenham
Dr A.R.J. Boggis
Gordon Bohn
Dr and Mrs Geoffrey Bond
David and Jenny Booth
Mrs K.E. Boreham
Cyril Boroda
Dr John Bostock
Mr and Mrs M.J. Bound
David Bousfield
Mrs Angela Bowe
Dr Ronald A. Bowen
K.E.J. Bowers
Mrs C. Bowley (née Tucker)
Brendan Bracey
D.E.C. Bradley
Elizabeth Bradley
Eugenie Bradley
Dr F.M. ('Derek') Braines
Dr T.K. Brandreth
M.I. Breekveldt (Martin)
R.S.E. Brewerton
Mrs Janet F. Bridge
Bronwen Bridges
Robert Brinley Codd
Dr David Britton
Mona and Julian Britton
Mrs J.E.R. Brixey (née Geldard)
Dr J.B.S. Brooks
Dr J.P. Brougham
Mr J.P. Browett
Mrs Ann Brown (née Bates)
Anne Brown
John James Brown
Dr K.F.C. Brown
Pauline C. Brown
Pauline W. Brown (née Symes)
Derek Stanley Browne
Gillian Browne
Dr and Mrs M.J. Brueton
Mary K. Bruford
Marjorie Brundrit (née Wood)
Ruth Elizabeth Stoney Bryans
Jane Bryce (née Colston)
Peter Buckley
Mrs Margaret Bull (née Olding)

Mrs M.P. Bulley (née Wood)
Sarah J. Bunkhall
Dr Edward H. Burgess
Denise Burley
Simon Burling
Miss B.B. Burnell-Jones
Alec Burnett
Margaret B. Burton
Mrs Olive P.M. Burton
Alison M. (Pickard) Bush
Mrs Joanna B. Butler
Janet Butlin
Andrew G. Butters
Bernadette Eileen Buxton

Alma E. Cadman
David Archibald Orkney Cairns
Mazie M.E. Calcutt
Mrs Nora M. Callow
Mrs J. Cameron
Dr Heather Campbell
Mr and Mrs Patrick Campbell
Dr and Mrs Sandy Campbell
Miss M. Campbell Gray
Dr Caroline Canfield
Kay M. Canning
Norman Capstick
Heather Caresani
Sarah Carew-Jones
Jennifer M. Carley
Miss Catherine Carlyon
Naz Carrington-Brown
M.B. Carson
Elizabeth Carswell
Marian Carter
Mr Paul G. Carter
Mary Caspell (Waterhouse)
Jean Cass
Deborah Cassidi (Pollock)
Michael J.D. Cassidy
Arthur Casson
Dr and Mrs John Catlin
R.E. Catling (née Martin)
C.A. St. C. Catterall (née Robertson)
Mrs Elizabeth Catto
Mrs Angela M. Cave
Marguerite Cédard
John Challis
John Chalstrey
Susan Chalstrey
Douglas and Jennifer Chamberlain
Patricia M. Chamberlain
Frances Chapman
Miss Heather Chapman
Dr. J.R. Chapman
John Chapman
Peter Chapman
Prof. Tim Chard
Dr M. Charlesworth
Vera Charter (Strang)
Dr and Mrs P.A.B. Cheetham
Fiona M. Cherry
Dr Robert Chesney
L.J. Chisholm
John A. Chivers
D.M.A. Choi
John A. Cholmeley
Mrs Christopher Gareth Church
Prof. Anthony Clare
K.A. Clare
Mrs Susanne Clare

Mrs Jeannette Claridge
Miss Julia Sharon Claridge
Beryl Clark
Lorna J. Clark (née Wakefield)
Daphne M. Clarke
J.M. Clarke
Margaret Clarke
Sylvia Clarke (Birrell)
D.H. Clason-Thomas
Dr Elmer Clissold
Elizabeth M. Cloutier
Eric Clow
W. Clunies-Ross
P.C. Cobb
Ann Cochrane (Tribbeck)
Hilda A. Cocks (née Broughton)
Eleanor Coë
Frank Coffin
John E. Coggle
Dr Vivienne Cohen
Dr P.A. Coldrey
Dr and Mrs A.G.H. Cole
Judith Cole-Jones
Ruth M. Coles
Dr P.C. Collinson
Dr John Coltart
Nora Coltart (Hensley)
Dr P.R. Connell
Dr Brendon Conry
Elizabeth Constable
Barbara A. Cook
Mrs Beryl M.M. Cook
N.K. Cook
Richard C.M. Cook
David A.P. Cooke
Mrs Jean Cooke
Julie Cooke
Anna Cooper
Dr Jane Cooper
Jennifer Copeman
Dr and Mrs Ralph Corbett
Dr T.R.J. Corner
Valerie Cornford (née Blackwell)
Mrs Christine Costello
Mrs A.B.E. Cotton
Dr Terence Graham Coupland
Geoff and Mary Court
Rupert Courtenay-Evans
Mike and Rita Courthold (née O'Sullivan)
Jeanette Coutts (née Moore)
Miss A.F. Cowan
Patricia Claire Cox (née Dakeyne)
Dr Patrick J.N. Cox
Theresa L. Cox
Mrs Jeanne Cracroft
Pamela V.M. Craft
Mrs V. Crawford
S. Criddle
Colin M. Cripps
Simon G. Crocker
Ruth Croker
Mr and Mrs M.L. Crosfill
Sally Crosher
Joy Cross
Miss Judith Crossley
Dr A.N. Crowther and Mrs J.M. Crowther
   (née Durling)
David Cunnah
Eilis Cunningham-Davis
Marigold Curling
Dr Peter Curtin

C.E. Custerson
Dr Dan Martin Cuthbert
Miss Mary Cuzner

Joan Dallas
Miss Mary Dalton
Sylvia G.S. Darker
Miss Ruth Darvill
Dr Satya Sundar Das
H.K.M. Dastur
Angela Davey
Captain David Davidge
Dr Arwel W. Davies
Gerald and Helen Davies
Isabel Davies
R. Kerry Davies
Prof. Robert J. Davies
Mrs M.J.C. Davis
Mrs P.E. Davis (née M.J. Burnyeat)
J. Davy (J. Roberts)
Alexander Michael Dawson
Dr and Mrs Antony Dawson
D.A. Dawson
Mr Adrian C. Day
Angela Day
Margaret C. Chappell Day
Shirley D. Daynes
Jill de Sausmarez
Elizabeth H. de Spiganovicz
Dr Martin P. Deahl
Dr D.W.J. Dean
Leonard Charlton Dean
Audrey R. Delafield (née Ronaldson)
Josephine Denman
Celia Dennis
Hilary Jane Dereham
E.M. Dewe (née Oliver)
Caroline M. Deys
Catherine M. Dickens
Mr A.J. Dickinson
Dr and Mrs S.R. Dickson
Professor Paul Dieppe
Paula Dillingham
Dr and Mrs Roger Dixey
Dr A.K. Dixon
Mrs Judith Dixon
Pamela Dobson
Paul and Caroline Docherty
Angela and Anna Dodd
Mrs Jean Dodds (née Church)
J.S. Dodge
Helen and Roger Doherty
Maureen Doherty
Dr and Mrs Robert Donaldson
Brian Doney
Magdalen Donlan
Barry R.H. Doran
M.J. Doresa
Dr G.S. Dormand
Eric Dormer
David Dorrell
Andrew Ernest Dossetor
Peter Doughty
Mrs E.M. Douglas (Jean M.C. Foster)
Mr and Mrs M.A. Douglas
L.N. Dowie
Len Doyal
G.H. Patrick Drake
Rosalind H. Droy
Dr and Mrs T.P. Dudeney
Samantha Dunk

Marjorie R. Dunlop
D.M. Dunn
Lois Dunn
Mr W.D. Dunsmuir
Mrs Pat Durkee (née Ball)
Maureen Dyke (Blanc)

Ann K. Eades
Elisabeth G. Eades
A.M. Eady
Dr Douglas H. Eaton
Stephen R. Ebbs
Dr and Mrs A.D. Edelsten
Professor Tim Eden
Mrs Jenny Edmonds
Dr Philip Edmondson
Dr D.R. Edwards
Helen Edwards
Mrs J.S. Edwards
Judith Edwards
Vivian Edwards
Mrs Paddy Egerton
P. McA. Elder
Shirley Elder (Page)
David and June Elliott
Mrs Helen Elliott (née Shepherd)
Mr and Mrs L.E. Ellis (Elizabeth Ogilvie)
M.A. English
Mrs A. Evans
Mrs Angela and Miss Jane Evans
Clive M.W. Evans
Daryl Evans
Judith A. Evans
Mrs Pauline M. Evans
Rachel Evans
Mrs Shirley M. Evans
T. Arwyn Evans
Patricia Eve

L.M. Fahey
Peter D. Fairclough
Constance Fairhall
Mrs Patricia Falcini
Mrs J.J. Falczyńska
S. Farrant Russell
Mrs Maryann Farrow
Dr and Mrs P.R. Farrow
Mrs Sue Fawcett (née Rowe)
Kerry Fawcitt
Mr and Mrs Ian Fearnley
Dr T.C. Fernie
Dr and Mrs C.R. Fife-Schaw
Jean M. Filby
Dr Pierre and Mrs Ruth Filletti
D.R.A. and G.A. Finch
Margaret A. Finch
Mrs D.L. Fingleton
Mrs Carole Finlay
Dr and Mrs R. Finlayson
Tim and Sue Finnegan
J.R.H. Fisher
Jean Fisher
Geoffrey R. Fisk
June Flann (Williams)
F. Mary Fletcher
Dr John and Mrs Judith Fletcher
Alison L. Forbes
Clara Forbes (née Brown)
Mrs J.C. (Sue) Ford (née Morgan)
Mary A. Ford
Dr Richard Foskett
Dr J.M.G. Foster

Dr Richard C. Fowler
Sara Fox
Alan and Sally Frame
Mrs K.D. Franklin
Frederick E. Fraser
Dr and Mrs Clive Froggatt
Dr and Mrs C.A. Fuge
Alan P. Fuller
A.E. Fyfe

Doreen M. Galbreath
Linda Galpin (née Stewart)
Mrs Cynthia W. Gandy
Zena A. Gardner (née Shaw)
Mr D. Garfield Davies
Anne Garland (Strickland)
Miss Janet Garland
Dr Adrienne Garner
Francesca Emma Garnham
John Claude Garnham
Percy Cyril Claude Garnham
Pamela Gaskell (Thorne)
Mrs M.M.L. Gavan Duffy (née Bowers)
Jeffrey Gawler
Jennifer Gaze
M. Susan Gaze
Dr Mark Gaze
Dr Shane John George
Christine Mary Gibbons (née Wilson)
Jennifer Gibson (née Exell)
Margaret Gifford
James and Sandy Gilchrist
John Michael Langton Gilks
Rosemary Gill (née Morris)
Mrs V. Gill
Bryan and Margaret Gillett
O.J.A. Gilmore
Cedric and Jean Gilson
Mrs J.M. Ginn
Dr Michael E. and Mrs Mary J. Glanvill
Dr Terry Glanvill
Judith Gledhill (née Cowley)
Dr Peter Goldberg
Fiona Goldsmith (née Harding)
Dr Norman Golledge and Sylvia Golledge
   (née Wampach)
Irene C. Gomersal
Dr R.M.H. Gompertz
M. Goodacre
John Gooddy
Dr Kate Goodgame
Dr M.E. Gore
Mrs P.D. Goulding
Miss Elsie M. Gover
John R. Goves
Malcolm Graham
Gerald J. Grainger
Dr C.B.T. Grant
Mr Michael Grant
Sandra Gravestock
Dr·Mrs A.G. Gray
Jean Gray (née Jessiman)
Margaret P. Gray
Doreen R. Green
Gabrielle W. Green
Hilary Patricia Green
N. Alan Green
Dr S.A. Green
A.W. (Sandy) Greer
Dr and Mrs George Greenhalgh
K.L. Greenhalgh
Mrs Elizabeth Greenwood

Katharine M. Grice
Richard H. Griffith
Carol J. Griffiths
Mrs Eileen Griffiths (née Riches)
Ellis Rhys Griffiths
Evan Griffiths
John D. Griffiths
Professor and Mrs Paul Griffiths
Prudence Griffiths and Hilary Jones
Mrs Rosa Griffiths (formerly Hayward)
Mrs Patricia Grigsby
Robina Grime
Dr Thomas A. Grimson
Dr Edwin Robert Grover
Mrs Lorraine Elizabeth Kelly Grover
Susan J. Grunstein
Mrs Louie Guerin
Dr Victoria Joy Guest
Dr John B. Gurney Smith

Veronica Hackett (Gardner)
G.J. Hadfield
Stephen Hadfield
Mrs Suzanne E.J. Hadfield
Dr John Hale
B.D. Hall (née Hiscott)
Mrs D. Hall Brooks (F.I. Jeans)
The Hall-Smith Family
Mrs W.J.A. Hall-Turner
Miss Kathleen Halpin
Mrs Anne Hambidge
Dr John Hamer
Elizabeth M. Hamilton
Dr Gervase R. Hamilton
Mrs Daphne Hamilton-Fairley
Ann F. Hammond (née Hoyle)
Joyce Hammond
Dr William J. Hanbury
Shirley Hando
Mrs A.M.T. Hannah
Mrs Joanna Hardie (née Glossop)
David J. Harding
Joan Harding
B.M.H. Hardman
Roy Harfitt
Mrs Joan Harford-Rees
Michael Harmer
Michael and Jane Harmer
D.R. Harper
Dr Michael Harrigan
Caroline V. Harris
Dr and Mrs D.M. Harris
Mary Harris
Mrs Mary Harris
Miss Monica Harris
Pamela Harris (née Woollard)
Patricia Harris
Dr Patricia Harris
Ruth Harris
Mrs Greta Harrison (née Summers)
Keith R. Harrison
Rosemary Hart
Dr Sarah Ann Hartill
Dr K.W.D. Hartley
Alison E. Harvey (née Webb)
J.V. Harvey Kemble
Lesley Harwood (née Humphreys)
Michael T. Haslam
Mrs Lucinda Hassell
Melanie Hawes
Dr J.D. Hawkins
Dr K.M. Hay

Ann Hayes
Dr G.T. Haysey
Stanley Frederick Hazelton
Dr and Mrs C.E.D. Hearn
Joy Heffernan
Dorrienne Heine
Barry Hemphill
Margaret Henderson
Dr C.E. Henry
Margaret Henry
Jim Herold
Ralph Heyland
Mrs Jean Heyward (née Sawers)
Professor Bryan Hibbard
Jillian A. Hibberd
Roger Hickling
Dr G.E. Hicks
Philomena Higgins
Jean Highmoor
Mrs Anne Hill
Christine M. Hill
Dr D.A. Hill
Ian M. Hill
Mr R.A. Hill
Anne Hillier
Margaret Hills
Esther C. Hindley
Tony Hinds-Howell
P.M. Hirst
Jack Hoadley
Dr Mary E. Hamer Hodges
Catherine Hodgetts
Pat Hodgkinson
Mr S.L. Hodkinson
Malcolm C. Holbrook
J.F. Hollingshead
Heather M. Holmes
Mrs J. Holmes (née D.J. Wilkinson)
Miss D.E.K. Holmes-Higgin
Diana Patricia Holroyd (née Hogan)
Beryl Holtby (née Eyre)
Adene Hooton
Catherine Le.Coyte Hopkins
Dr Angus Hoppe
Miss Leigh Hopwood
Sara Horler
Amelia Muriel Horsey
Jill Horton
Michael A. Horton
Albert William John Houghton
Nicholas B. Houghton
Mrs G.B.B. Howat
Dr J.B. Howell
Dr and Mrs D.B.M. Howells
Dr Sean Frederick Howlett
C.N. Hudson
Ruth Hudson (née Mander)
Anne Hughes
Audrey Hughes
Mrs Fiona Hughes
Dr Mervyn S. Hughes
Susan M. Huizenga
Mrs W. McLean Humble (E.R.H. Morley)
Rosemary A. Humphery
Dr. M.J.N. Hunt
Dr P.G. Hunt
Louise E. Hunter
Dr and Mrs Barry Hurn
Helena Hurndall
Dr G. Huston
Mrs M.K. Huston
Mrs H.V. Hutchinson (Nothnagel)

Dr Peter J.A. Hutchinson
Mrs D. Hutchison

Daphne Ince
G.S. Innes
Lawrence M. Iregbulem
Dr A. Iversen

M.E.W. Jack
Frances L. Jackson (née Ramsden)
Gerry and Frankie Jackson
Ian M. Jackson
Dr John Jackson
Philip A. Jackson and Irene H. Jackson
Dr P. Jakeman
Barbara James (née Lloyd)
Derek C. James
G. James (née Christian)
Matthew James
Siân M. James
K.F. Jamieson
Jeremy R. Jarvis
Christina Jaques
Madlen Jefferiss
Prof. D.J. Jeffries
Mrs Caroline Jemmett (née Claridge)
Professor J.S. Jenkins
Jane E. Jenkins (née Probert)
Mrs K. Jenkins (née Lyons-Montgomery)
Miss Laura Diane Moses Jenkins
J.A. and M.G. Jennings
Christopher J.A. Jephcott
Prof. Norman Joels
Alun John
Andrew Johnson
Ian Johnson
Joan M. Johnson
Jonathan R. Johnson
Dr S.M. Johnson
Daphne Johnston (née Hoyle)
Mrs Susan Johnston
Donald Joines
Miss Belinda Michelle Jones and Mr Nigel
    Edwards
Drs Carwyn and Sarah Jones
Dr D.H. Jones
Dennis and Nora Jones
Mrs Gail Jones
Lyn Jones
M. Beryl Jones
Dr Steve Jones
Dr W.K. Jones
Miss Martha L. Jordan
Dr Anthony P. Joseph
Dr J.H. Gordon Jowett
Nigel I. Jowett
Dr Michael Joy
Richard Juckes

Dr Peter W. and Dr Jeffrey R. Kaplan
Jean M. Kay
Tibor Kaytar and Jane Kaytar
Drs David and Louise Keeling
Dr I. Kelsey Fry
Dr Brian R. Kendall
Michael and Jan Kennedy
Mrs S.A. Kennedy
Miss Margaret Kent
Dr Gervase N.W. Kerrigan
Jonathan B. Kersley
Pamela Kidd (Evans)
Gladys Kidner

Wendy M. (Thompson) Kielly
Trevor Kimm and Frances Kimm
Mrs Enid P. King
Dr Peter M. King
Valerie King
Dr Peter King-Lewis
Dr Judith Kingston
Sheila M. Kingston
Sue and Ted Kirkham
P. Anne Knee
Mrs Jane Knight
Mrs Sally Knight (née Erith)
Mrs H.A. Knight-Olds (S.M. Pope)
Dr J. Knill-Jones
Miss P.M. Knowles

Tony Labrum
E.F. Laidlaw
R.G.B. Laidlaw
Helen S. Lambourne
Dr F.A.P. Lander
Mrs Jane R. Langley
S.E.M. Langley
H. Heber Langston
Professor and Mrs Richard Langton Hewer
Miss Jill N. Last
Elaine and Christopher Law
Malcolm Law
Alison F. Lawrance
Kingsley Lawrance
Mrs Brigid Lawrence
Dr David Lawrence
Hilary Lawrence
H.A. Laycock
Elizabeth Layton Jones
Anne P. Leather
Jane and Peter Leaver
Anne Leinster
Isabel Lemon
Susan Lennard
Alan Lettin
Miss B. Levack
Pamela A. Levy
Dr R.G. Lewin-Smith
Miss Brenda Lewis
Dr C.A. and Dr G.M. Lewis
Mrs J.M. Lewis
Dr John H. Lewis
Dr Gerald Libby
Mark I. Liddington
Mrs D.M. Lindsley
Roderick and Jane Line
John Charles Linley-Adams
Dr and Mrs Michael Linnett
Dr Richard and Mrs Ann Livings
Dr Bethan A. Lloyd
David A. Lloyd
Claire and Alan Lodge
Mrs B.A. Longford
Elizabeth C. Lonergan
Jamshid Lotfi
A.E. Lough
Mrs Sheila M. Lovell
Dr David Lowe
Jane R. Lowe-Forrest
Dr Brian and Lady Margaret Ludlow
Dr A.H. and Dr A.C.M. Luscombe
Dr Mark Lynch
Sally Lyon
W.C. Lyon
Janet Lyons

Dr Francis Ian Macadam
Mrs Sylvia Macaulay
Mr and Mrs M. McBride
Mrs Lesley B. McCartan
Dr Mark A. McCullen
Mrs Joan McDonald
Joy McEwan (née Biggs)
Helen M. McEwen (Launders)
C.E. Macfie (née Reeks)
Neil Gilbert McGuire
Heather Machin
Mrs Helen Macintosh
Dr John W. Mack
Dr and Mrs Angus Mackay
Gordon Cameron Mackay
Dr P.J. McKenna
Olive Mackenzie
Dr R.K. Mackenzie-Ross
Marilyn and Alan McKinna
Dr Charles Mackworth-Young
James McLaughlin
Mary Maclaurin (née Boniface)
Alison McLean
Tom and Vicki McNicholas
Sheila Macvie
Mary Maggs (née Mothersill)
W.M. Maidlow
Prof. and Mrs J.S. Malpas
Janet Mann
B.D. Markwell
Jonathan J. Marlow and Emma L. Hurst
Dr Brian T. Marsh
Maria Martinez
Richard J. Mascari
Alan and Jane Mason
Jane E. Mason
Dr K.R. Mason-Walshaw and Mrs E.J.
    Mason-Walshaw (née Elsey)
Dr Alan Massie
Mrs Fiona Mathias
Eileen M. Matthew
Dr Sarah Matthews
Mrs Margaret F. Mavroleon
Mr A. Richard Maw
Katharine Maxwell
Elizabeth Mayberry
S.B. Mears and J.A. Cook
Mrs P.A. Medhurst
Joan Medlock (née Heitland)
Dr V.C. Medvei
Mrs Joan E. Meikle
Pamela M. Mellis
Mrs Ann Menzies
Dr John J. Messent
J. and D. Meyrick Thomas
Dr George W. Middleton
Dr Harry Middleton
Mrs Pamela M. Middleton
Susan Middleton (née Crabbe)
Rita M. Miell
Carole Miles (C.E. Pickles)
Christopher and Louise Milford
Lenox J. Millar
Dr Michael W. Millar-Craig and Dr Janet
    A. Millar-Craig
Helen Millard
Mrs A.D. Miller (Sims)
D.L. Miller
Elizabeth Miller
Jean Miller
Dr and Mrs Richard Miller
Ronald A. Miller

Mrs Sheila C. Miller (née Wilson)
Dr and Mrs H.E. Milligan
Joan, Viscountess Mills
Dr Peter Mills
Dr Ian and Mrs Tina Milne
Julia Mingay
Sandy Mitchell
Prof. David Moffat
The Hon. Mrs A.C. Mole
J. Monckton
S.K. Moody
Drs Jennifer and John Moon
Mrs Susan Moore
Dr John Moore-Gillon
Mrs Lynn C. Moralee
Eileen O'Fee Moran
Dr Barbara L. Morgan
Dewi J.R. Morgan
Julie Morgan
Mrs Monica Morgan
Mrs Jane Morley (née Epps)
Mrs F.I. Morris
Dr and Mrs G.C.R. Morris
Dr and Mrs J.Ll. Morris
Margaret C. Morton (née Ewen)
Mrs Margaret Moss
A.J. Mowan
Dr David and Mrs Mary Moynagh
Dr B.J. Muir
Mrs B.M. Muir
Dr and Mrs P.D. Mulcahy
Josephine Mules
Lindsay Jane Mulligan
Dr and Mrs James Mulvein
Chris Murcott
Beryl Murricane
Ms Valerie Musson
Beryl C. Myers

Mrs D.A. Naylor (Jede Green)
Mrs Heather Neale (née Yeadon)
Dr Rachel E. Need
Yolanda Negri
Mr and Mrs John K. Nesbitt
Judith Nettle
Marian Nevell
Alexander Munro Neville
Mrs Daphne Neville
Roger Garstang Newberry
John Clifford Newbold
S.M. Newbold
Mrs Hazel Alice Newcomb
Doreen Newson (née Eales)
Sally Newton
W.D. Nichol
Dr B. Clive Nicholson and Mrs T.F.E.
    Funnell (Nicholson)
Dr. L.A.K. Niemiro
Mr and Mrs P.A.R. Niven
Margaret Nixon (née Innocent)
J.G. Noble
Eric Noren
Miss D.S. Norman
W. Norman-Taylor
Mrs Joyce Norrish
E.E.A. Northridge (Atkinson)
Aubrey Norton Hill
R.E. Nottidge
Gwen Noyes

J.R. O'Brien
Mary and Guy O'Donnell

Margaret Rose O'Fahey
Dr Brendan and Mrs Sarah O'Farrell
Nigel Offen
Dr Catherine Offer (née Lloyd)
Dr and Mrs William Stewart Ogden
Tony O'Kane
Dr Leslie David Ormerod
Dr and Mrs T.P. Ormerod
Fiona E. Orr
Kay Osborn
Jennifer Osman
Ray Osmont
Mrs M.F. Oswald (née Eastman)
Dr and Mrs D.G. Owen
Joyce Oxborrow

Judith Ann Pain
Dr Kenneth R. Pallot
Mr C.A.L. Palmer
Valerie Pamment
Douglas Park
Mrs G.W. Parker
Jane Parker
Phyllis M. Parker
Robert B. Parker
Vicky Parker
Dr Norman Paros
Hugh Parry
Dr John Lloyd Parry
Mr and Mrs Robert Paton
Maureen M. Patrick (née Pearson
Dr Fram Patuck
A. Dudley Payne
Ann Payne
Mrs J.M. Payne
Mrs Rebekah Peacey
Edward Pearson
Dr R.M. Pearson
Jennifer Peiser (née Cooper)
Dr James Pemberton
Dr Nigel William Penfold
Cicely Perrotte (née Qualtrough)
Mike and Judy Perry
Dr Marko Petrovic
Mary C. Pettegree
Mrs Shelagh Phelps
Mrs Pamela Ann Phenna (née Shorter)
Mrs Celia C. Phillips (née Hanford)
Dr Claire P. Phillips
Dr E.H.D. Phillips
Len Phillips
Ms Mari Anne Phillips
Dr Mary Phillips
Dr and Mrs Simon Phillips
Ursula Mary Phillips
Katie B. Philpott
Maurice G. Philpott
Patricia Piccirillo-Myers
Claire Elizabeth Picton
Josephine Pike
R. Pilkington
Allen Pilling
John Pilling
Dr Chris Pinchen
Mary F. Piper
Dr J.M. Pitt
Dr N.M.F.P. Pitt
Mrs H.L.J. Pitts
Dr Malcolm Pleydell and Mrs Jeannette
    Pleydell (Ball)
Joan M. Plumridge
Mr J.R. Pogmore

E.M. Poll
Dr Kristin Pool-Whalley
S.F. Poppitt
Miss Margaret Potter
Mrs Eunice C. Potts (Wright)
Deborah A. Povey
John M. Powell
Josephine Price
Susan Price
Dr J.J. Prior
Mrs J.J. Procter (M.F. Reid)
Henry Proctor
Dr and Mrs Ian Proctor
Mrs Barbara Pullen

B.E. Quiggin

Margaret Raban-Williams
Jenifer Raimes
Mrs M.M. Raincock (née Arthington)
Peter A.M. Raine
Mrs C.J. Raithby-Veall
Dr G.J.E. Rash and Dr N.K. Allanson
Mrs D.M. Rasor
Sheelah Mary Ngaio Rattray
Peter and Katy Ravenscroft
Dr Robin Rayner
Mr Laurence Read
Mrs V.H. Read (Eakin)
John P.D. Reckless
Dr Auberon Redfearn
F. Redknap
Susanne Mary Castleden Redmond
Dr and Mrs P. John Rees
Professor Linford Rees
Dr A.J.M. Reese
Kirsteen Cazalet Reeve
Mrs Sue Reeves
Mrs D.A. Reggler
N.S.C. Rice
Mrs D.R. Richard
Billie and Stephen Richards
Colonel J.C. Richardson
Miss L. Richmond
T.O. Rahere Rimmington and Peggie
   Rimmington
Yvonne Ristich
Jean Ritchie
Janet Robb
Mrs J. Robert
Barbara L.M. Roberts
Evelyn Roberts
R.M. Roberts
Miss Samantha J. Roberts
Shirley W. Roberts
Alistair C. Robertson
Carol Robertson (née Moseley)
Sheelagh Robertson (Kellock)
James O. Robinson
Mrs Joan Robinson (Tyrer)
Lena Robinson
M.L. Robinson
Mrs Margaret Robinson
Mrs Rebecca Robinson
Dr C.S.B. Roch-Berry
The Rev. Dr Richard T.B. Rodgers
Jackie Roe
Ruth Roe
Simon Roger
Dr Bill Rogers
Frances Rogers and Dr V.A. Crawford
Dr and Mrs John Rogers

Mrs R. Mary (Rowland) Roome
Catherine Phelps Rosen
Kenneth R. Ross
Dr Peter Dallas Ross
Douglas Rossdale
Dr Steve Rousseau
P.G. Rowe
Dai Rowlands
Paul Rowntree
Eileen Rubenstein
Dr Michael Rule
Margaret and Andrew Rumsey
Christopher Ruoss
Dr and Mrs A.L. Russell
Mr and Mrs I.D. Russell
R.S. Russell-Smith
A. de la C. Russian
Anne Ryan

Mr J.E.L. Sales
G.P. Sampson
Mrs Barbara Saulez
Mrs Pamela Sawtell
J. Howard Scarffe
Dorothy P. Schuman (née Smith)
Adam Scott
Mrs Joyce Scott
Dr and Mrs Simon Scott
Dr W.C. Scott
Professor Sir Eric Scowen
Margaret Scurlock
Mrs D.W. Seldon (née Fells)
Patricia B. Selfe (née Laing)
M.M.C. Selley
Anne Selwyn-Smith
Dr Andrew Seymour and Mrs Susan
   Seymour
Dr B.E. Shairp
William S. Shand
Clifford Hamer Shaw
J. Shaw
John H. Shepherd
Diana Sherlaw
Mrs Louise Shipfield
Alison Simmons
Jean Helen Simmons (née Stewart)
Dr Paul Simmons
Mrs Anne H. Simon
Kenneth Simon
A. St J. Simpson
E.A.D.W. Simpson
Peter Simpson
Dr R.I.D. and Mrs J.E. Simpson
Kathleen Sims
Andrew Skanderowicz
Mrs B. Slade (née Windridge)
Professor Gerard Slavin
Peter and Valerie Sleight
Mrs E. Sloman
Mrs Joan Smailes
G.I. Small
Gillian Small
D.H. Smallwood
Ann Smith (née Rivett)
Elizabeth Smith (née Ronald)
Evelyn M. Smith
Jean D. Smith
Mrs Lisa Smith
Roderick and Phillida Smith
Sue Smith (née Jones)
Dr Diane P.L. Smyth
Dr N.J.C. and Dr B.J. Snell

Mrs Marion Soep (Roger)
Mrs Angela Sokol
Mary Somerville (née Butterworth)
Dr P.J. Southall
Dr and Mrs R.H. Soper
John and Madeline Sorrell
Trevor and Sue Southey
Miss E.V. Spencer
Jane Spencer (née Biddle)
Dr and Mrs K.P. Spencer
Pam Spouge (Lawrence)
Johnnie Spreckley
Glynis Sproston
Mrs Caroline Spurrier (née Warwick-
   Brown)
Dr David Stainton-Ellis
Gillian Stalder (Barraclough)
Dr A.F. Stallard
Dr R. Stanhope and Ms Carol Every
   Stanhope
A.G. Stansfeld
Edna M. Staple
Mrs S.E. Stearn
Mrs R.V.C. Steevenson (D.P. Royal)
C.S.M. Stephen
John and Prilli Stevens
Elizabeth Mary Steward (née Bailey)
Dr D.A. Stewart
Mrs Ann Stobbs (née Doherty)
Mrs T. Stockdale
Dr B.E. Stone
Evan Stone
Audrey Northcott Storm
Dr Peter Story
Kenneth E. Strangleman
Deborah E. Stratton
H.J.M. Stratton
David F. Street
R.A. Stroud
Mrs Susan C. Stroud
John L. Struthers
Barbara Strutt
Ronald Stubbings
Pamela M. Stubbs (née Massy Collier)
K.G. Sugden
Judith Sunderland
John and Rosemary Sutcliff
Mrs R.H.A. Swain
Valentine A.J. Swain
Andrew and Dorothy Swanston
Gary A. Sweeney
Peter and Meg Swinstead
Lynette Sykes

Dr and Mrs P.M. Tabor
Geoffrey Tamlyn
Dr Peter Tatham
Dr G.L.V. Tatler
Patricia A. Tayler (née Rowe)
Dr Andrew L.J. Taylor and Mrs
   Madeleine H. Taylor
Mrs Ann Taylor
Mr and Mrs C.N. Taylor
Mrs D.M.C. Taylor
George Rowland Taylor
Jean Taylor
Olive Muriel Taylor (Rollin)
Dr. T. Taylor
Joanne Teece (née Hobson)
Yvonne Terry
B.M. Thacker
Dawn Thatcher

Mrs C.C. Theodosius and Miss C.M. Theodosius
Dr Barry Thom
Dr D.W.P. Thomas
Dr Gareth Thomas
Mr Keith Thomas
Mary Thomas
Owen G. Thomas
Mrs P.J.C. Thomas
Elizabeth Thompson
Dr Graham Thompson
Nicholas V. Thompson
Suzanne Marie Thompson
Yvette Thompson
Dr P.E. Thompson Hancock
James P.S. Thomson
Dr Napier Thorne
John L. Thornton
Mrs Cynthia J. Thorpe
Miss Suzanne L.F. Thorpe
Glenice B. Tickle
Mrs Elizabeth Tindley
M.C. Tinniswood
Pauline M. Tinsley-Holly
Dr and Mrs J. Toby
Robert McL. Todd
Mr and Mrs Iain S.W.S. Tollemache
Celia Tomkins
Claire Tomkins
Dr and Mrs R.J. Tomlinson
Dr C.R.V. Tomson
Mrs S.M.E. Townsend
W. David Tredinnick
Dr R. Treharne Jones
Jean Trend
Dr Christopher Trower
Dr Gareth Tuckwell
Sally Turnbull (née Elder)
Geoffrey Turner
Dr John C. Turner
Professor Paul Turner
Peggy Turner
Dr P.S. Tweedy
A. Twining (née Brodie)
Miss E.K. Tysoe

Geoffrey Udall
Jill Urwin
Dr C.W.J. Ussher

Dr Julian Vahrman
Patricia Vallender
Patricia Leese van de Kasteele
Nancy and Pat van de Linde
Maxine L. Van-Toller
C.K. and M.N. Vartan
Mrs Oriel Hobbs Vazifdar
Julie Venables
Dr Peter Venables
Dr Clare C. Vernon
Dr and Mrs Raymond Vickers
Peggy Vidler

Judith Waghorn
Ian Waldin
Mrs A.P. Walker (M.L. Sullivan)
Florence Walker
Mary Walker
Dr R.W.H. Walker
Antony Francis Wallace
Marguerite Evelyn Waller

Mrs Janet Walne
Joanne Walpole
Jill Walter (née Thomson)
Mrs B.A. Walters
Jean Walton
Joan Wampach
Sheila M. Ward
Dr and Mrs A.J. Warsap
Professor John Wass
Mrs Gillian Waters (née Stow)
Professor William Estlin Waters
Mr Martyn Waterworth
Dr G. Watkinson
David Watson
Dr John U. Watson
Dr Adrian L. Webb
Mrs G.M. Webb (Sandra Wells)
Judith A.W. Webb
Jane Webster
Mrs Mary Webster
Rachel M. Wege
Margaret Anne Welch
R.H. Welch
Michael A. Weller
Ruth Welles
Dr J.T. Wellingham
Irving Wells
Mrs Patricia Wells
Julien Wenger
R.A.L. Wenger
Pamela Wertheim (née Bacon)
Mary Margaret Westall
Nicholas V. Western
Mr Peter Weston
Mary Wharton
The Reverend Michael and Mrs Shirley Whawell
Irene A. Wheeler
Ann White
Mrs B.R. White
Dr David R. White
Peter M. White
Sheila Whitehead
Rodger Whitelocke
Christine M. Whitfield
Hugh N. Whitfield
Sarah Whitfield
S.W. Whiting
P.T. Whitman (Barker)
Miss K.A. Whittam
Dr and Mrs A. Whitworth
John and Ann Wickham
David J. Wilkinson
Barbara Williams
E.A.V. Williams
Mr J.D. Williams
M.E. Williams
Mr and Mrs P.K. Williams
Dr C.J.F.L. Williamson
Dr P.F. Willis
Mrs Willmott (W.B. White)
Derek Willoughby
Mrs Sally Wilmot
Dorothy Wilson (née Bale)
Mrs E.M. Wilson
Joy Elizabeth Mary Wilson
Dr M. Wilson
Mr and Mrs M.C. Wilson
Sally Winship
Miss Joanna Winston
Kenneth Wise

Melanie G. Pollard Wise
Mary C. Wiseman (Ruoff)
Barbara Witcomb
Dr David Withnall
M.P. Wolfe
Dr B.L. Wood and Dr D.N. James
Margaret Wood
Professor R.F.M. Wood
Dr Susan M. Wood
Mrs Mary L. Woodcock
Helen M. Woodiwiss
Marjorie Woodroffe
Amelia and Michael Woolmore
David and Julie Wright
Eileen A. Wright (née Flewin)
Mrs F.M. Wright
Mrs G.P. Wright
Dr William J. Wright
Mrs Marion Wrightson
Dr Graham Wylie and Dr Elaine Wylie
Olive Mary Dunn Wyllie
Ann Wyndham (née Evans)

Dr C.J.P. Yates and Mrs J.A. Yates (née Hall)
Rosemary Yates
Ronald Lam Soon Yeoh
Edith M. Young (Stapley)
Miss K.E. Young

Dilys and Ron Zeegen